Tales of the
CASELOAD

JUSTIN JONES | RITA HYDE - JONES

ABOUT
THE AUTHORS

Justin Jones is currently the Deputy Director of Community Corrections for the Oklahoma Department of Corrections, which includes probation and parole and other community-based programs. He has 26 years of correction experiences including probation and parole officer, District Supervisor of Oklahoma County Probation and Parole, Interstate Compact Officer, Warden, Regional Director of Institutions and Deputy Director of Probation and Parole. He has been published in several newspapers and in Corrections Today magazine. Justin has been an elected delegate to the American Correctional Association, past conference chair for the Correctional Accreditation Managers Association and president of the Oklahoma Correctional Association. He has also presented workshops for the American Probation and Parole Association and the International Community Corrections Association training conferences. Justin has degrees in sociology and journalism. He currently serves on the board of directors as a regional representative on for the American Probation and Parole Association and is a committee member for the American Correctional Association Parole Committee.

Rita Jones-Hyde acquired a B.A. at Oklahoma State University and an M.A. at the University of New Hampshire. She is currently a doctoral candidate in English Literature at the University of North Carolina at Greensboro. As a child, she lived in various locations in Oklahoma as her father, Justin Jones, moved up the probation and parole ladder. While growing up, she was exposed to the workings of the justice system and to the stories of her father and his friends. Her exposure gives her a unique viewpoint of the personal and internal lives of probation and parole officers while her education allows her to write about her experiences.

ACKNOWLEDGEMENTS
AND DEDICATION

The authors would like to acknowledge and say thank you to American Probation and Parole Executive Director, Carl Wicklund for his encouragement and assistance in bringing this book to reality. We would also like to say thanks to Linda Sydney for suggesting sample chapters be sent to APPA and for her sincere laughter while reading said chapters. Our goal of entertainment was achieved.

The authors would like to dedicate this book to those professionals who have served before us and will serve after us in the art of probation and parole supervision. For it is through their hard work and dedication in facilitating offender pro social behavior, that risk is reduced for all of us.

Table of CONTENTS

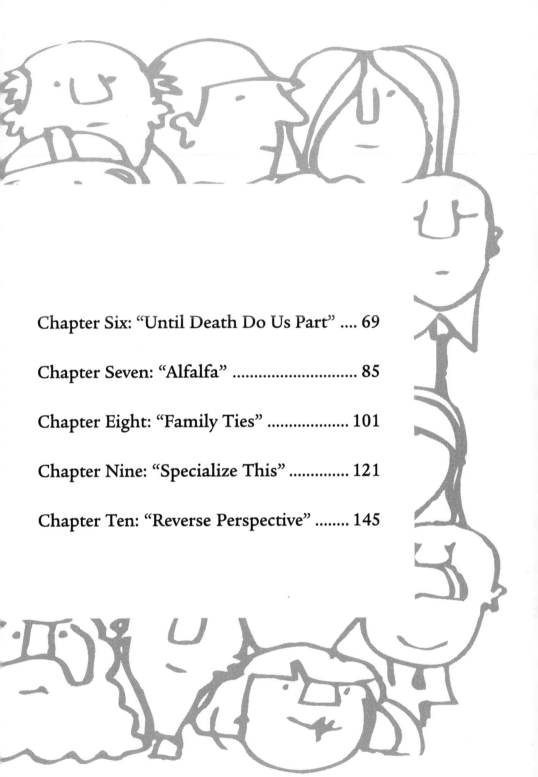

INTRODUCTION

Tales of the Caseload is a series of narratives based on fact and immersed in fiction.

The stories combine humor and seriousness, attempting to entertain and educate. This book is designed to provide a satirical learning experience for probation and parole officers and to feed the public's curiosity about the everyday accounts of community supervision. Of course, we also hope to entertain readers who read the book as a pastime or hobby.

To illustrate the accounts of various officers, the stories are divided by chapters. Narrators, including tenured agents Jack Toliver, Jake Pruitt, and Danny Reeves as well as rookie Mr. Jones, describe the internal workings of probation and parole and provide a personal rendition of their situations. *Tales of the Caseload* follows their metamorphosis from uninformed and naïve officers straight out of college to seasoned veterans educated in the field. The officers and the readers learn from the interesting and entertaining descriptions of encounters and characters. The reader will be also introduced to colorful probationers and parolees absconding and reporting as they go skipping down the yellow brick road of community supervision.

The tales border on fiction only in the sense that names have been changed and dialogue has been altered. In some instances, we have fictionalized direct quotes because we simply cannot recall the actual statements. Even though some part of each of the stories is fiction, the main body of the text is based on fact.

Chapter One
"The Awakening"

I saw him sitting there after I had turned, locked the door, and proceeded down the stairs. Since I had just eaten a quick bowl of shredded wheat in silent solitude, as to not wake my wife and six-month-old daughter, the last thing I was expecting to find was someone at the end of my three-step porch. As this unexpected stranger threw the butt of one cigarette into my yard and proceeded to light another, he looked at me and said, "I've done a bad thing." Though I didn't recognize him, his shirtless back decorated with an array of ink blue tattoos had some familiarity. Again he said, "I've done a bad thing." The glow of his unfiltered Camel cigarette grew brighter as he took an enormous drag, inhaling a forest of smoke. My eyes locked on his mammoth arms, and I finally recognized him. This man, Doug Wade, was a parolee on my caseload.

I had been a probation and parole officer for only six months when I found Doug on my doorstep. In those days, officers were required to give out their home phone numbers, but it was an unwritten rule that people on your caseload didn't call you at home unless it was an absolute emergency. Only such things as "I had a court order to call you" or "I just won Publishers Clearinghouse, and I need to pay off my restitution" constituted an emergency. Even though I had a caseload of about 200, consisting of probationers, parolees, and an assortment of other forms of creative sentencing, none had ever greeted me at home, and none has ever since.

Dismayed at Doug's presence, I was at a loss for words. Do I ask, "What the hell are you doing here?" Do I simply ignore him and go to work? Trying to keep my cool, not to mention my head, I calmly queried, "Doug, what is so important that it couldn't wait until the office opened?"

He didn't answer but slowly handed me a butt of blue steel, a .357 caliber handgun, from over his left shoulder. He handed me the gun without rising or turning to look at me. I wondered if it was the October breeze that caused the chill to crawl across my back, or the fact a convicted felon had given me a gift. Unsolicited and for some unknown reason, I was now the proud owner of a weapon that could inflict mass destruction. I believe CNN later copyrighted the phrase, "Weapons of Mass Destruction."

The weight of the gun and my gut reaction determined that the weapon was loaded. What should I have done with it? There were several options, and I'm sure while reading this you thought of some possibilities.

What should I have done?

A. Placed it casually in the front of my pants, pointing it toward my crotch?
B. Said, "No thank you. I already have one," and returned it?
C. Thrown it as far as I can?
D. Said, "No thank you. I'm trying to quit."
E. Accepted it, told him to wait right here, and gone inside the house to call my supervisor for advice.
F. For those of you who are peace officers, practiced shoot or don't shoot.

Which one did you choose?

I leaned up against the porch rail in order to create the illusion that I was comfortable with Doug's presence and the circumstances he presented. "Okay Doug, you've done something wrong, you've handed me a weapon, and now don't you want to tell me what the hell is going on?"

Doug removed the Camel long enough to make one statement. "Oh man, I screwed up. This dude got my gas, and I shot him."

While Doug secured the half smoked cigarette in the corner of his lips, I stood there waiting for the additional information I needed to understand his predicament, a predicament that had now bled over into my life. And yes, bled was the proper description as bleeding and my blood were certainly in the forefront of possibilities. Since I've always been uncomfortable with pregnant pauses, and this one felt like a marathon, I studied Doug's gestures.

He stood and turned to face me but didn't make eye contact. I was a young probation officer, both in age and experience, but I knew that many of my clients didn't make eye contact during serious conversations. I assumed it had something to do with prison etiquette or low self-esteem. Or, perhaps, eye contact was avoided when a lie was about to begin. Since Doug was ignoring my glances, one or all of the above reasons could apply. Anyway, this young parolee, who bares a striking resemblance to the lead singer of the Foo Fighters, was facing me. With his weapon dangling by my side and my stomach in knots, I said, "Doug why are you here?"

Wasn't that brilliant? I had just asked this man one more time why he was here after he had already told me. His foot making circles in the dirt, eyes staring downward, thumbs leveraged in the waistband of his 501 Levis, Doug swayed back and forth like a first grader caught throwing chalk.

"Mr. Jones, I shot him."

Doug was a man of few words, and once again I patiently waited through another record-breaking pause in this fragmented conversation. Finally, he shouted, "The son-of-a-bitch had it coming! He stole my gas!"

Drawing from my vast experience and training in interpersonal skills, motivational interviewing, and verbal judo, I gave him my best come back. "What?"

Doug removed his left thumb from his waistline long enough to expertly flick his cigarette. It went tumbling through the air, arching at about ten feet, and landing on the hood of my 1969 Camaro.

"I shot him," Doug murmured.

I was more concerned at this point about the burning cigarette on my car's hood than what Doug was saying; however, once again, my sharp communication skills took over. "You shot a man! What the hell for? Don't you know you'll go to prison for that?"

For the first time since I opened the door to head for work that morning, Doug looked up at me from the bottom of the stairs. "Guess I screwed up," he said. "Guess I just wasn't thinkin'. All I could think about was that I had paid for my gas, and this dude is pumping my gas into his car. Man that pissed me off. I said to him, 'don't you know that's my damn gas, and I'm late for work?' He just stood there like some fool, holding the gas hose and looking at me like I was some kind of *crazy*. I told him, 'give me five dollars or I'm going to spank your ass right here for the whole world to see.' He just looked at me. So, I shot him."

Doug didn't need to explain the gas situation because I was all too familiar with the shortage. In the late 1970s, gasoline was supposedly in short supply, and the price per gallon had skyrocketed. I was part of the majority who felt the problem was a government conspiracy. This alleged deficiency and price increase had resulted in a sharp rise in the theft of gasoline at the pump. The medium-sized town that I worked in was no exception. The quick stops and other companies selling gasoline introduced the creative method of pay first, then pump. The problem with the new pump method was that many times you strolled inside to pay and someone else would mistakenly pump your gas after the store clerk had authorized the purchase based upon your payment. I describe all of this to provide those of you who were not old enough to drive or buy gas in the late seventies an opportunity to know what the rest of us had to endure. Anyhow, this same scenario happened to Doug.

After waiting through countless pauses, all I got was a burst of information that was as fast as it was short. I blurted out the next most obvious question, "Is the man you shot okay?"

He looked at me as if he had been a witness to the dumbest question ever coming forth from man.

"I don't know," he replied. "You can't stick around to check things like that out. You got to move and move fast."

It was obvious this conversation was going nowhere. I would learn later in my career about cognitive thinking and how it applies to criminal thoughts and activities. For now, I was on my own. Doug's thought process was certainly different than anything I had experienced. He had surrendered to the ultimate solution by shooting a man who may have made an amendable mistake. It was too late for corrections.

"So you are unsure about how bad this man is hurt or even if he is still alive?" I said.

Doug assumed his favorite position by looking down and replied, "He just looked at me like I was crazy after I shot him."

"What you're saying Doug is that this man never changes expressions from looking at you as if you were crazy before and after you shot him," I summarized.

"Yeah, so I got my gas and got the hell out. I was almost to work when I remembered I was on parole for armed robbery and that I needed to tell you when I screw up, so here I am."

I was starting to get a headache from Doug's surprise appearance and the thought that he was only here to tell me he had committed a crime.

"You know that question on that report you have me fill out every month, the one that asks if I've been arrested in the last month. Well, I wanted you to be the first to know I think I'll be arrested."

Doug was starting to loosen up now as he continued to close out his story.

"I don't really care if I go back to prison or not. I just don't want to screw this parole thing up. If you don't violate my parole, then it won't run wild with my new conviction for shooting this dude. So, I thought I would come find you, you could explain to the cops what happened, tell them this dude was asking for it, and with all this cooperation I would get a break. You know I could do a couple of years in prison standing on my head, but more than that drives me crazy."

Doug went on to tell me how this dude had a neck tie on that in some way contributed to the shooting, but I'm not sure how. It may have something to do with class differences or symbols of authority. Whatever the case, we were now getting somewhere in this story, and we were arriving to a much anticipated position where my level of assertiveness or lack thereof would play a pivotal role in the future direction of this meeting.

At this point, I could run away screaming or stay and be fearless. I chose to be fearless. Having limited previous experience with offenders, I acted on the first plan that exited my mouth. In the most assertive yet caring voice I could muster, I said, "OK Doug, let's go to the sheriff's office and get this thing straightened out."

Since state cars hadn't been introduced yet, we walked toward the Camaro. Doug commented on the cherry red color of my "nice ride," as he called it, and removed the now defunct cigarette butt resting on the hood. As we started to drive off, I realized Doug had the aroma of a leathered old man devouring tobacco. Needless to say, I quickly drove the few blocks from my apartment to the courthouse, which contained all of the county offices and jail.

We passed the army of gas pumps on the boulevard and parked in the drop-off zone. We were a site to behold as we exited the car and proceeded up the steps to the sheriff's office: Doug with no shoes, which I hadn't noticed before, and I with a large weapon tucked safely in the front of my pants. Doug had to give up his package of Camels before pleading guilty to "Shooting with Intent to Kill," and receiving a 15-year sentence. The wounded business man at the gas station was seriously injured but made a full recovery. I survived, never filled out an incident report, never told my wife until years later, and met Doug again when he paroled after two years.

Chapter Two
"The Naked Truth"

I've worked in two-person offices and large metropolitan agencies. Both settings have advantages. In small towns, where probation and parole officers are higher up on the food chain of the justice system, judges listen to them and sometimes call them for advice, and prosecutors let them hang out in their offices. On the other hand, large metropolitan probation and parole bureaus allow officers to utilize assistance from fellow employees and give them someone besides clients to talk to all day. There is also something to be said for the anonymity available in large offices.

It was my "duty day" in a department of 70 officers and a few short-handed support staff. The usual mayhem was churning. The waiting room was abuzz and bulging with a potpourri of society's misfits, opportunists, anarchists, homeless, mentally ill, sociopaths, and, yes, attorneys. In the chaos, it was hard to separate the misfits from the opportunists and the anarchists from the attorneys. As the duty officer, I had the honor to visit with most of these characters, and, in fact, I had the *privilege* of serving them.

This day started like all the other "duty days." Several officers called in sick, we were short on clerical workers, and the usual fire drills occurred. The crankiest judge in the county called and dramatically inquired about a pre-sentence investigation report which, by the way, was due *yesterday*. Three police officers requested addresses for suspects from my caseload, and the computer system refused to work. By ten in the morning, the system was still down and the police officers had called to inform me that one of the addresses I provided was a vacant lot. Even though I apologized for not performing the required initial home contact, deep down in the pit of my stomach I knew the officers were seriously questioning my abilities and referring to me as something with long ears, hoofs, and a tail. The furious pace continued as I wrote receipts for probation fees, restitution, and a dozen other requirements. When noon arrived, I was deep into the world of multi-tasking.

In the hectic world of caseload management, it may not always be possible to provide advance notice to clients when leaving or changing caseloads. Sometimes it can be cost prohibitive. Grant wasn't one of the officers who had called in sick but, in fact, had transferred to a new unit. As a steady stream of his clients formed in the waiting room, I realized that Grant hadn't processed notifications of his transfer. I tried to process Grant's clients with priority because changing officers can be traumatic. Following the initial influx of parolees on their lunch hours, I broke the news to two of his clients. They seemed elated, but insisted Grant was the best officer they ever had. After assigning these two clients to new officers, more of Grant's clients waited for their turn to see me, Super Duty Officer.

Our waiting room was expertly decorated with the Governor's, Lieutenant Governor's, and the Director's pictures hanging on the walls. Besides the state royalty, our waiting room displayed life-sized images of the best state parks the continental United States had to offer. The frames were tattered, the pictures faded but it was the thought provoking essence of it all that mattered. Underneath a picture of the Grand Canyon, one of Grant's female clients sat, staring out in space, with her back straight and arms folded, as if she was waiting for the prom's first dance. She didn't wear make-up and had her hair curled into a bun. Her legs were chalky and her sandals worn. Since she was sitting patiently and appeared to be under little or no stress, I saw Grant's clients who fiddled in their chairs, as if waiting for an execution, first.

I saw Jeff the career thief, who was self employed as a truck driver. He owned his own rig and was about $110,000 in debt. He seemed happy enough for someone who had felony theft charges pending in another state for "borrowing" trailers of wheat. Jeff confessed his innocence as I made a note to his new officer that a violation report was needed.

Then there was James, the aging playboy, on parole for bigamy. His fading playboy bunny tattoo was a dead give away that I was encountering the answer to every woman's desire. However, James was deteriorating like a humor that only my grandfather's generation could appreciate. He smelled of his once-a-week bath, his diesel cologne, and a fine dusting of good earth.

After assigning the aged Hugh Heffner to a new officer, I finally visited with the stoic young lady whom I assumed was waiting for her monthly jolt of checks and balances, not to mention a good dose of parole officer advice and wisdom. I greeted her in the waiting room with a brief introduction and my customary hand shake.

"Who are you?" she calmly asked as her ebony eyes peered at me.

Emulating her attitude, I said, "My name is Mr. Jones, and I'm the duty officer today." She showed no interest in my position and didn't introduce herself.

"I don't need to see you," she said. "I'll wait for Mr. Grant Wilson. He is my probation officer, and I don't want to talk to you."

My vast experience kicked in. I quickly ascertained that the waiting room wasn't the place to tell this lady about Grant's departure. So I responded with an appropriate diversion, "Come on back to my office, and we'll see if we can't find Mr. Wilson."

Yes, I manipulated the truth, and, yes, those uninitiated in the ways of probation and parole might call me a liar. However, it was all done to control the chaos of the waiting room and the immediacy of the situation.

She followed me down the long corridor, a hallway with synchronized openings on both sides leading through the mysterious world of probation and parole supervision. Cautious, yet steady, she walked several feet behind me, stealing quick glances into any office with an open door. For a civilian, those doors hid the mystery of the system, and I noted why officers frequently closed them. Of course, I knew her name, but thought, perhaps, she would introduce herself as we walked towards my office. She didn't. A little conversation would have shortened the journey.

After what seemed like the longest walk of my life, we arrived safe and sound in my office. She immediately moved her eyes from side to side, scanning my office and taking particular interest in my bookshelf. She also peered at the Dr. Martin Luther King Jr. quote framed and placed on the wall and a Native American painting depicting a woman's metamorphosis from a human into a spiritual butterfly.

She then sat down and started to shuffle her feet on the floor. Her sandals almost fell off in the process. She was clearly uncomfortable and gripped the chair for support. Wanting to keep our meeting as short as possible, I retrieved her file and other pertinent information as expeditiously as possible. The management information system was slow, but I was just happy that it was now working. I only wanted to review the status of court related obligations and last reporting date because I liked to leave the case plan review and any other possible assessments to the office of records. The role of a duty office certainly didn't include unsolicited assistance in these areas.

The file had just appeared on the computer screen when she asked me in a business tone, "Where is my officer?"

Without looking directly at her, I replied "just a minute."

About a nana second, if there is such an increment of time, was all it took for me to realize that she required a more detailed response. Before I could read her court cost status, I was confronted with yet another stern statement.

"You can't 'just a minute' me. I don't have a minute."

Once again my keen probation and parole officer skills kicked in as I ascertained this could be a critical point in our newly established relationship. "I just wanted to take a moment to view your file to see if there was anything we needed to discuss," I replied.

She rolled her eyes in disbelief and began tapping her fingernails on the arm of the chair. "Mr. Wilson should be here 'cuz I made an appointment two weeks ago. Is he sick or something?"

Now was the time for a critical decision. Would it be wiser to say "yes, he is sick," or "he went to lunch" or would the truth best serve this situation? Not weighing my comments carefully enough, I responded, "Well, Mr. Wilson isn't available today."

"What does that mean? Does that mean you don't know, or you know and won't tell me?"

I was preparing to tell the truth. She appeared to be an intelligent client and would understand that her officer was assigned to another office across town. I pondered how difficult it would be for her to adjust. Even though all officers aren't the same, the process of supervision was fairly consistent. I decided to complete this duty officer contact and assign her to a new officer. I was about to inform her of my decision when the unpredictable interceded.

Without even knocking on the door frame, Officer John Abernathy stepped into my open door and graciously promenaded into the office to announce that the inmate crew from the local work release facility had arrived to transport Grant's last two file cabinets to his new office.

I've never closed the office door while visiting with a client of the opposite sex; however, I would've braved the repercussions in order to keep Abernathy from blurting out ill-timed information. Now it was too late to shut the door and reverse the clock, and it was obviously not a fitting moment to tell Mr. Know-It-All Abernathy that he was incorrect. I had worked with Abernathy for years, and we had an unspoken code that we shared with most of the office. Duty officer contacts didn't require a restrictive level of officer interruptions.

In other words, Abernathy could barge in as many times as he liked without suffering the consequences. He knew the rule all too well and quickly departed. I also knew the rules, and Abernathy would suffer with or without an unspoken code.

Since pauses weren't my forte and I felt this one was going to last full term, I moved like a top in slow motion into my best probation officer, time to get down to business, posture. I had a genre of positions for every occasion. There was the "half-way reclining, yet still paying attention" position for those time consuming client visits where I lost interest in the first five minutes but just couldn't find an opening to close out the visit. Then there was the infamous "lean forward," where not only was the chair pulled up to the table, but I also leaned slightly forward on my desk. This positioned allowed me to have the upper hand during sessions where a firm statement was needed. Also, pushing my hands on the desk and sliding my chair back to a principal position was effective.

I scanned through my usual positions and decided on a new approach. I swiveled my chair around, placed my left hand under my right elbow, and stroked the newly constructed beard on my chin. From this position, I was prepared for any statement Grant's client could make. This position gave the impression that I was attentive, yet decisive and in deep thought, yet able to block any forthcoming blows. I was now in a position to confirm Abernathy's outburst and break the news to Grant's client.

Before I could expand on Abernathy's breaking news, I was preempted by the woman's astonishment. "Mr. Wilson doesn't work here anymore?"

"He has been transferred," I confirmed.

Her aura quickly changed. She squashed her eye lids into a thin slit and projected an intensely serious glare in my direction. With her mouth hardly moving, she ordered through her teeth, "I need to see Mr. Wilson now!"

I couldn't offer her much. I told her that I was sorry that Grant no longer worked in this office, that I missed him too, and that she could see her new officer today. I wasn't using my planned direct approach because I wanted to maintain control of the situation.

"I want to see Mr. Wilson. Now!" she demanded.

It was time to move to the next level of control. She was going to have to understand that unless she was assigned to a small office or to an officer in a rural setting, changes occur. The high rate of officer turnovers in metropolitan areas and boundary changes often force clients to change officers. It was just a fact of life.

I had the strange feeling that she didn't want my reasoning. I asked her if she understood that Grant had moved to a new location and wouldn't be able to be her officer.

"Oh, I understand. You are the one who doesn't understand. I need to see Mr. Wilson."

Realizing that this client meeting was going nowhere fast, I decided to cut my losses and move on to the next contact. As duty officer, I had to maintain my position and keep the lines moving. Therefore, I responded, "Go ahead and fill out this monthly report and when you come in next month, your new officer will see you."

She shoved the monthly report form towards my side of the table, crossed her arms and the stand-off commenced.

The 120 ticks of the clock informed me that the silence had gone on long enough. She also noticed, and, like dinner plates used as cymbals, she interrupted the pause.

"I am not leaving until I see my officer," she demanded.

Now it was time to display the authoritarian demeanor all probation and parole officers possess. I, the "jack of all trades," decided to demonstrate respect in this situation and address her by her name.

"Ms. Liz Brown," I interjected, "do you not understand that it isn't possible today? I can give you his new phone number. If you must speak to him, you can do it later."

I mentally patted myself on the back and thought, "There, that should do it." I had met her defiance head on and the new phone number had even given her a small victory.

At this point I didn't care if Grant wanted to speak to Ms. Brown or not. The waiting room was growing more crowded by the moment and my name was echoing down the corridors. "Mr. Jones, you have a duty officer contact in the waiting room," the receptionist blurted out time after time.

I'm not a patient person and the pressure to resolve this situation was increasing. I had to throw down the gauntlet. "Ms. Brown, I do not mean to be disrespectful, nor is it my intentions to appear to be uncaring. I understand that clients sometimes become attached to their officers and that's fairly natural. However, in this case, we have no options. Mr. Wilson can no longer be your officer. I have given you the option of calling him later and even have offered to provide the phone number. So, fill out this monthly report and let's move along. I have other people waiting."

Before I could gather my next thoughts, Ms. Brown stood up and stated, "Oh, I don't have options? I'll show you options."

With that and one quick movement, she reached for the top of her pullover dress. The next moment she was naked. Ms. Brown laid down more than my gauntlet.

Before I could regain my speech and determine why she wasn't wearing any underwear, Abernathy returned. "Shit! What the hell are you doing?" Abernathy blurted out. From where he was standing in the door way, I couldn't determine if he was asking me or the naked woman.

"We obviously have a situation here," I responded stating the obvious.

"We? You damn sure do."

All this time, which was only a few seconds, Ms. Brown stood in a defiant stance.

"Put your dress back on," I demanded.

"I'll put my dress on when I see Mr. Wilson."

I knew the rules related to hostage taking and how to act if I was held against my will. The department even had a handbook on the subject and a mandatory annual training class. My first thought was how I hadn't been trained in this type of situation. Nudity was not in the handbook.

My second thought was how I could sue for failure to train and how do I get the hell out of here? While I questioned my career choice, Abernathy made his exit and swiftly returned with several staff members. They made snide comments and stared. We all stared. The audience stared at Ms. Brown, she stared at me, and I stared at my socks, wondering why I had worn unmatched socks today. I looked up occasionally to see if Ms. Brown was still there. She was and was covered in powder from head to toe.

Everyone in the crowded doorway tried to give advice. Several officers wanted to arrest her. Several others wanted to call 911. Abernathy and some of his friends joked about forcing clothes on her. Martha, the saint of the office and the oldest of the officers, offered Ms. Brown a probation and parole field jacket, the brand with "Officer" on the back and a badge emblem on the front. Ms. Brown, the experienced and street smart client, refused the field jacket.

Since none of the options appealed to Ms. Brown, who kept repeating her demand, I said, "Look everybody, I got this under control."

"We can see that," echoed a voice from the back of the crowd. I leaned in the chair and, once again, scratched my chin contemplating which option would be the most effective in this situation.

> *Would it be:*
> A.   Leave the room and let Martha handle this.
> B.   Allow Abernathy to use force to clothe Ms. Brown.
> C.   Call 911 and allow the police to handle this and laugh at us.
> D.   Wait this thing out because she would eventually freeze.
> E.   Call Officer Wilson.
> Which one would you choose?

I chose to negotiate. "Ms. Brown, if you will put your dress on, I'll call Mr. Wilson."

"When Mr. Wilson arrives, I'll put my dress back on." The upper hand was hers.

While the standoff continued, the audience depleted until only the female officers remained. The office protocol eliminated any additional male participation and viewing. Only I, the lone male officer who everyone now blamed for this situation, was left. I could see the blaming in their eyes. I could see the laughter just beyond the curvatures of their vibrating lips. I had to give in a little.

"I'll call your officer and ask him to come over, but I can make no promises or guarantees that he will come," I humbly said.

With this, she turned away from me only for a moment while she pulled a chair up to my desk and stated, "I'll wait." And wait she did.

Martha chose to stay with me and Lady Godiva. Martha reached over, picked up a *Corrections Today* magazine, and passed the time as if she was waiting for a doctor. She even appeared to be actually interested in what she was reading. Meanwhile I placed the call to Officer Wilson.

"Yes Grant, you heard me right, Ms. Brown is over here in my office now, naked, and demanding to see you. NAKED! Look Grant, I don't have time for this, just come over here quick," I demanded.

While I listened to Grant make humorous comments about me getting my underwear into a twist, Martha shut the door and asked Ms. Brown about the powder. Ms. Brown looked at Martha in an effort to determine her sincerity. Martha has always been congruent with her clients and I guess Ms. Brown sensed Martha's empathy. Grant's client explained that the powder was to keep her smelling fresh between tricks. She thought that we knew she was a prostitute. They continued to chat, and Martha led the conversation into the direction I was most curious about.

"Why is it so important for you to see Mr. Wilson today?" she asked.

While Ms. Brown started to explain, Martha took the jacket and placed it around Ms. Brown's shoulders. She accepted the coat and embraced it as if she was freezing.

I was vindicated. I knew if I hadn't had interference, I would have frozen her into clothing submission.

Ms. Brown told Martha that all she wanted to do was thank Officer Wilson for referring her to an employment agency and a shelter several months ago. She had taken full advantage of the referral and had been doing fine. However, a substance abuse relapse had forced her back to the street. She wanted to explain the new situation to Grant and ask him to visit her employer because she had been fired the week before.

When Officer Wilson arrived, Martha stayed, and I left as soon as Ms. Brown put her dress back on. I went back to my duty officer rounds, correcting the chaos in the waiting room.

Later, a shelter staff member arrived to assist and place Ms. Brown. Of course I had to write an incident report and attempt to get Abernathy to write a statement to back up my comments. I also had to endure a lecture from my supervisor on proper duty officer etiquette and endure the jokes, ridiculing e-mails and nudist colony enrollment forms I received from my beloved peers. However, the most difficult thing was realizing I had a lot to learn about human dynamics.

Chapter Three
"Silent Night"

I leaned back in my swivel chair, which no longer swiveled, and placed both feet on the edge of my desk. I was ready for the weekend. The week had been furious, and I was mentally drained from all the activity, not to mention recording my entire end-of-the-month statistics. Since an accounting for all duties on my caseload was required, I had to total my office, field, and collateral contacts, and calculate the percentage of clients who were employed, students, or disabled. I had to record arrests and court dates as well as anything else the administration felt would complicate my life.

If only the public could understand the multiple tasks involved in probation and parole officer's balancing act. One moment I was an accountant collecting restitutions, probation fees, and other financial obligations. The next moment I was a counselor attempting to be attentive and caring when clients explained why they were unemployed, divorced, arrested, quitting GED classes, or applying for an interstate transfer. In addition, unexpected duties always required my expert attention. All of this was why I was kicked-back with my feet on the desk, staring out the window and waiting for the weekend to arrive.

"One more hour," I contemplated, "just one more hour."

I twisted and pulled at the tattered cloth on the seat cushion. My chair had long ago descended past the point of fiscally responsible repair. Through my window, I saw a group of officers chewing or smoking their nicotine vice. I understood my parents' addiction to these death sticks because they were raised during the great depression and my father was in the military. During those years, the government promoted the use of cigarettes as an avenue for relaxation and the chewing of tobacco as a mechanism for coping with the times. As far as I could determine, these officers had no excuse and were setting a bad example for their clients. I watched as the rising smoke created monsters drifting towards the afternoon clouds. I was mesmerized. I felt time slip away and my consciousness fall into a wistful floating sensation. I dozed off, but only for a moment.

"Danny! Danny!" I heard but didn't quite comprehend someone yelling my name. However, the ensuing kick that caused my elevated and well rested feet to fly off my desk awakened me quicker than a bartender's last call for beer. My quick reflexes sprang me upright before Jason could accuse me of sleeping.

"Do me a favor. I need to leave an hour early, and the boss wants me to do a pre-sentence interview at the county jail. I got a date, and you owe me a favor," Jason quickly rattled.

"I don't owe you anything," I sharply replied and returned my feet to their resting position.

Jason was one of those new officers: single, unorganized, and manipulative. He had been an officer for about two years and pushed everything to the limit, especially the dress code. His supervisors scrutinized his spiked hair and sideburns, and today, "casual day," Jason had once again pushed the limit.

On the third Friday of each month, for a dollar donation to a departmentally approved charity, staff could wear denim and other non-traditional office attire. Most of the staff dressed similarly to my clothing, a polo shirt and non-faded denim complimented by casual shoes. I chose on this particular Friday to wear a pair of Doc Martins while Jason Cooper, as usual, stretched the boundaries of good taste. He wore a pair of bell bottomed painter's pants that were three sizes too large and had unraveling seams at the leg bottoms.

I didn't understand why he would wear utility pants with a loophole for pliers and a slot for a hammer. The pockets were big enough to hide a litter of Dobermans. To compliment his pants, he wore a bright tropical shirt with the shirt tail protruding past the pant inseams. Also, he had on a pair of 1970s tire tread sandals with socks.

Even though Jason gave casual day a bad name, I liked him all the same. Despite his unconventionality, he was a good officer and had the respect of his clients and his co-workers. With a crooked smile and an irresistible coolness, this fashion beast stood awaiting my response.

"What favor?" I asked. "I don't owe you any favors. If the truth be known, you owe me. Besides being brain dead, I was thinking about leaving a little early."

"Look Danny, don't you remember around last Christmas? Your wife was looking for you, and I was duty officer. I believe you were at The Red Rooster quenching your thirst with the rest of the office, and you guys left me here to cover. I had to tell your wife you were working hard and late in the field," Jason retorted.

Jason was spinning his web of guilt, and I was having none of it. "Yeah, I remember that. But come on, telling my wife I was working late isn't comparable to conducting a pre-sentence interview in the county jail on a Friday afternoon at quitting time. Besides, its casual day, I can't go down there lookin' like this."

"OK, OK, I see," Jason replied. "How about the time I covered the back door while you attempted to arrest that so called 'docile client?' You assured me he wouldn't run, and it would be a quick trip. Do you remember?"

I nodded in agreement, wishing he wouldn't bring up that old story again. "He ran out the back door, knocked me down, and jumped the neighbor's barbed wire fence. It wasn't until I caught up to him that I realized he was naked and apparently hadn't made a clear high jump over the fence. The only benefit was that there was no need to frisk him. How embarrassing, having to parade this naked and wounded man back to the car. Then there was the blood I cleaned off the back seat after the transport. Did I mention all of this in the incident report? No I did not."

Since I already knew the story, I motioned for him to skip to the end.

He continued, "And then there was the time I told you to slow down because of a large drop off over the hill. But, no, you wouldn't slow down, and you ruptured the gas tank on our new agency car."

"OK! I get your point." I took my feet off the desk so that he could see my annoyance. "Why does this interview have to be today?"

"Danny, you don't want to know. The bottom line is Judge Morris won't grant another extension."

"*Another* extension?" I rolled my eyes.

"Well yeah, I had been looking for this dude, but how was I supposed to know he had a twin brother? They both have records and have pulled scams of identity before. I did the whole damn pre-sentence investigation before the district attorney called to warn me about the twin. I still wasn't sure if I had interviewed the right brother. I had to wait for fingerprints from the state police. By that time, the judge was pissed and locked-up the right twin. I told you that you didn't want to know."

Jason seemed stressed from the whole situation, and I wondered why I hadn't heard about it before.

I hated owing favors and could never remember when the markers were cashed in or when I was in debt to someone. Since Jason had certainly placed his chips on the table, I assumed I owed him.

"Alright," I said. "If you'll shut up, then I'll do it. Give me his name and court order and anything else that can get me in and out in a hurry."

Calculating my previous plans for the evening, I really had nothing to do. My wife might be expecting to go out to dinner, but I would have ample time for that. Over the years, I had done so many interviews that I could speed them up and compress the data like a zip file.

I enjoyed the new, trendy computer lingo. Zip this and zip that. I wanted to zip down to the county jail and zip this thing up before supper. After the little excursion, I planned to have a reward, a nice dinner with my wife, a plate of enchiladas, and a bowl of chips and queso from Garcia's Hacienda. As I tried to picture the Mexican dishes, Jason handed me the case file and trotted away in triumph.

I strolled to the west exit past the row of closed offices and towards the parking lot. Several of my fellow officers were loitering around their cars, rehashing some of the week's more colorful events and preparing to leave all this probation and parole glamour for the weekend.

Snuffing-out his cigarette under his foot, Buddy yelled. "Hey! Danny! Where you going with that file? Doing a little homework? You need to get some balance in your life."

"Oh, just helping out Jason. Doing a quick interview at the county jail," I responded.

"You're kidding me," Buddy laughed. "Jason has been trying to pawn off that interview all afternoon. I can't believe you bought that story about him having to leave early because an old girlfriend from high school is coming in. And I bet you bought the twin brother story hook, line, and sinker."

"No, no story here." I wanted to hurt Jason. "I'm just returning a favor to clean the slate. Besides, you know me. I'll be in and out of the jail in an hour or less."

I waved "good-bye" and walked away from my peers. Eventually, their entertainment at my expense faded in the distance.

I tossed the file into the front seat of my work car, a 1977 Chevy Chevette with more than 300,000 miles worth of quality probation and parole field work. The Chevette was my first new car. I bought it for its mileage rating, and it was all I could afford. When I bought the car, agency autos were in limited supply and most officers preferred to drive their own cars because of the sought after travel reimbursement checks. Fifteen cents per mile times an average thousand miles per month sure came in handy. It was like a second paycheck and almost as much.

The county jail was only three miles across town, just a block from downtown. The building, a fifteen story structure, was built a year earlier from sales taxes. When the first inmates moved into the facility last fall, the sheriff operated the jail.

However, there were many complaints, cost overruns, and escapes along with everything else that can break or burst on a large, new county jail. Also, following its construction, the local newspaper quoted experts who claimed the building was poorly designed and built. After much contentious debate, the sheriff was removed from his responsibilities and the county commissioners appointed a board of civilians and volunteers to oversee the facility.

Bids from private corporations were accepted, and an international company specializing in prisons was awarded the management contract. Since the company had never operated a county jail, problems like offenders being let out early and misidentified offenders appearing in court were common. My office had filed complaints against the jail about waiting times to see offenders and the general disrespect for probation and parole badges. Even with all these problems, I figured I could get in and out without a hassle because, after all, it was Friday evening.

When I arrived, I didn't expect to see a nearly vacant parking lot the size of Rhode Island. While I carefully parked the Chevette away from the other two cars, in an effort to not add to the thousand door dents it already had, I stared at the building, towering along side the other fortresses of the skyline. This red brick, limited window monstrosity, was a cross between The Tower of London and a bird cage for pterodactyls. The loosely graveled and pot holed parking lot was an extreme contrast to the new county jail.

Reaching across the gear shift for the case file, I realized, in my haste to leave the office and satisfy an I.O.U., I had left my jacket, badge, and identification in my office. Not to be deterred, I figured since my gift of gab had led me to the top of my profession, I could convince the central control jailer of my identity. Plus, most offenders could tell from my walk and talk that I was an officer. Confidence oozing, I strolled across the gravel and into the kingdom of felons.

Two jail trustees, polishing an already shiny white tile floor, greeted me in the foyer. The shorter of the two, the one with no front teeth and a mullet haircut, smiled and questioned me.

"Ain't you a parole officer?"

I assumed my walk gave away my profession. Trying to make small talk as we proceeded toward the front desk, I asked Billy Bob, as I called him, how he knew I was an officer.

"I sees your probation file you be carryin'," he grinned.

He hadn't even noticed my walk.

The second trustee, mopping his way over to me and chewing on a toothpick, stated "visitin' hours is over."

Being able to speak and keep a toothpick perfectly aligned ten millimeters from the right corner of his mouth simply amazed me. This janitor was well groomed and loved women. He had "MOM" tattooed on his left and right shoulders and "PEGGY" tattooed across his fingers. After acknowledging that "visitin'" hours were over, I carefully walked across the recently waxed floor towards the desk. The tattooed man went back to mopping, and Billy Bob shook his head. "You dumb ass! That there is a parole officer."

I peered through the bullet proof glass at the reception station only to find it was deserted. Like most motels, there was a buzzer fastened to the counter. I pressed it, and, unlike most motels, a deafening horn, the sound of a submarine preparing to dive, echoed down the foyer. A couple of seconds later I felt a tapping on my back. I twisted my body around and found myself staring into the chest of the largest human being I have ever met. I slowly looked up at his dented square chin and his sunken black eyes. He peered down at me, and I stepped away from him.

"Why you ringing the emergency line? You trying to cause trouble for yourself?" "Don't you know it's past time for visitation?" He questioned with a menacing tone.

In a cracking voice, twenty octaves higher than his, I responded weakly, "Yes, sir." Shaking my head and clearing my throat, "I'm a probation and parole officer, and I have a court order to interview one of your inmates...if that's okay."

"You don't look like a parole officer. Why you dressed like that?"

I described casual dress day to the officer who was wearing a newly starched uniform and spit-shined shoes. He just stared.

Thinking we had gotten off to a bad start, I motioned for a friendly handshake and proceeded to introduce myself. "Danny Reeves ... nice to meet you. I work at the south side probation and parole office." My hand disappeared into his.

"Sergeant Atkins." He wasn't pleased to see me.

I started the conversation again and showed him the file containing the court order to conduct the investigation. I was on a roll. I told him how long the interview would take and requested a quiet office. I didn't need anything fancy or elaborate; just enough room for the inmate and me to chat.

"You got any identification," he asked firmly. "You can't get in without an ID."

I explained how I was in a hurry and how I had left my badge and other forms of identification in my office. Since the mishap was entirely my fault I reasoned with him through logic. "I must be a probation officer. How else could I get this file and court order?"

Officer Atkins ignored my plea and, once again, asked for proper ID. He graciously referred me to section six, paragraph four of the operations manual. I explained that I knew the rules and that the manual could not predict every single instance in an officer's day. Noting his attempt to hold back a smile, I saw an opening in the conversation. With only one chance to convince him, I went in for the kill.

"Look, Officer Atkins, I'm willing to do whatever it takes to make this happen. I need to do this interview tonight. If you need to sit with me during the interview for security reasons, I'll understand. Handcuffing the offender isn't an issue. I can interview him between the bars of his cell. Just leave me in the hallway."

Sergeant Atkins rubbed the back of his neck, looked at the floor, and shook his head. "I'm the only one working at the moment," he said. "At this time of day we've already fed and locked everyone down. I can take you to, let's see, inmate Harjoe's cell, lock you in with him, and come back in an hour. Policy doesn't allow you be in the hallway unattended. Now you won't be able to take that file in there with you. We can't be having anything to build a fire with."

"Is that your final offer?" I joked. Sergeant Atkins didn't laugh. "Locked in a cell with no file? You can do better than that."

"No ID, bad clothes, late Friday, and no other guards. If you can get a better deal elsewhere, you should take it." I thought maybe, just maybe, he was making a mild joke, but I couldn't take that chance.

"Ok," I said. "We'll do this by your rules." I thanked him and patiently waited for an escort to the cell.

We strolled past the heavily secured administration area to an open elevator with padded walls. Everything smelled new. Not like the aroma of a new car but something created from essence of an old nursing home and fresh paint.

Unlike most new elevators I had ridden in, this one creaked, rattled, and shook all the way to the eighth floor. I practiced my best elevator etiquette. Step in, step to the back, fold my arms, look forward, and keep quiet.

When we came to a less than smooth stop, the stainless steel doors opened, revealing a cavernous eighth floor. To the left was a row of cells. To the right was a row of cells. In front and behind me were corridors of cells. I cautiously stepped off the elevator even though I wasn't sure why. I didn't need to be afraid. I had Officer Atkins with me. I had been in countless jails before even though I hadn't been in this one. The hall seemed quiet with polished floors, subdued bars, and dimmed light coming from the only windows in the hall-way. It looked like a 10,000 square-foot dance floor with rows of portable cages, both eloquent and ominous.

After taking in my surroundings, I turned toward Sergeant Atkins for additional leadership. He walked over to the vacant officer station, pulled a clip board off the wall, and began perusing a list of names. "This may take a minute. We haven't been able to get the computers up here to work. Gotta look up your inmate in this list," Sergeant Atkins spoke in an almost apologetic tone.

I stood waiting. From the elevator noise to our footsteps over to the officer's station, every inmate on the floor had noted our arrival. I could hear voices, but I couldn't determine from which direction they came. "Hey man, I'm out of toilet paper," cried one while another asked for his lawyer. "Got any cigarettes?" echoed down the corridor.

"Quiet on the floor!" Sergeant Atkins yelled.

The rustling in the cells came to an eerie halt. Silence was the name of the game, and I didn't need Einstein to explain why. Officer Atkins finished his search and called out for the prisoner.

"Inmate Kevin Harjoe?" No one answered. "Kevin Harjoe," he requested a second time.

From the very end of the hall to our left, a hand protruded through the bars with a come hither motion and an "over here" command. We had found our man.

I followed Officer Atkins down fifty yards of corridor towards Harjoe's extended hand. Along the way I received the usual questions: "Who the hell are you?" and "What the hell are you doing here?" In addition, Sergeant Atkins received his share of accolades and editorials, but all his calls were polite, of course. Had I not participated in casual day, I would have received more respect and fewer inquiries. In my normal suit and tie, the inmates would have confused me for an attorney. If such a mistake were made, I would have taken advantage of it because parole officers always need the upper hand.

My mind continued to wonder about such things as I glanced into the faces peering back at me. Friday night was definitely not a good time to take a tour of the new county jail. Inmates released on their own recognizance or prisoners who could post bail had already left for the weekend. Since the judicial system didn't work on Saturdays and Sundays, quick decisions and speedy hearings occurred on Friday afternoons. By Friday night, only poor, unfortunate souls with poor or no families were left in the county jail. Most weren't happy about the situation.

Within feet of Harjoe's cell, my attire took on a new meaning. Not only was I a stranger, but also the inmates considered me one of them.

"Little early to get busted on a Friday," observed a balding man in cell number ten. "Couldn't post bail?" questioned another. I apparently underestimated the effect of my attire. Now inches from Harjoe's cell, fate intervened.

"Officer Reeves, is that you?" I turned to see what remotely resembled an ex-client of mine. Trying to recover his name from the recesses of my mind, I whispered, "Yes." As that tiny word traveled through the air, the yet-to-be-named client jumped onto the bars of his cell. Even my new-found friend Sergeant Atkins rolled his eyes as this guy leaned on the bars and told tales from when he was on my caseload. He mentioned how he had gotten in trouble again, how he disliked his no-good officer, and how he was cheated out of an inheritance. Furthermore, he was charged with a crime and had found religion just yesterday. He kept talking, and Sergeant Atkins and I moved on.

When we arrived at Harjoe's cell, I didn't know what I expected to see; however, I did know that I didn't want to see six inmates. I had to count them twice: one, two, three, four, five, and six. These various vagabonds waited for Sergeant Atkins's command.

"Inmate Harjoe, front and center." There was grumbling as Harjoe worked his way towards the front of the cell. A tall, thin, and long haired figure cautiously approached us. Not looking up until his hand gripped the bars, I saw who was keeping me from my enchiladas.

"My name is Harjoe," a low voice resonated. I hastily assessed Harjoe's demeanor as lazy with extreme non-compliance potential. I wanted to hurt Jason. Harjoe wore a red sleeveless Pearl Jam t-shirt and hip hugger Levis, not seen in public since 1968. His Converse tennis shoes had more holes than my fishing net, and his untied and soiled shoe strings streamed at least ten inches behind him. He wore a backwards baseball cap with a peace sign button as a fastener and size adjustor.

"This parole officer needs to visit with you," explained Sergeant Atkins.

"Ok with me."

"Mr. Harjoe, I'm Officer Reeves, and I need to ask you some questions to complete the pre-sentence investigation ordered by your judge."

"You don't look like any parole officer I ever seen," replied Harjoe.

"I've been getting that a lot these days, but I really am a parole officer."

Sergeant Atkins removed a huge key from his belt ring and opened the cell door. I waited for Harjoe to exit the cell but no movement occurred.

"Well!" Sergeant Atkins motioned for me to step into the cell.

Surprised, I replied, "Well what?"

"Get in."

"Get in where?"

"Don't you need to interview Harjoe?" Sergeant Atkins questioned. He wrinkled his forehead to show his frustration. Since six inmates were waiting at the cell door, we needed to make progress and fast. I thought one more question would fix everything.

"In there?" I humbly asked while nodding my head toward the cell.

Sergeant Atkins and Harjoe both gave me the look, the look where everyone knows the rules of the game but me, the look where people can't figure out if I'm stupid or difficult.

"Here it is..." said Sergeant Atkins. "When there is only one officer on duty and I'm the one officer, my policy is for you to do the interview inside here, and I'll come back when you're finished. We had this chat earlier. You agreed. Now get in."

I thought for a moment. I didn't want to appear timid, nor did I want to appear insensitive to Sergeant Atkins's plight. I fought for what would be the most adequate response.

"Okay, I forgot," and I confidently promenaded into the cell, shook hands with Harjoe, and proceeded toward the only community property in the cell, a faded blue light special picnic table. As I sat down and felt the cold aluminum through my jeans, I noted the fake wood on the picnic table and prayed for heat. I could hear Officer Atkins close the cell door. I couldn't tell if the chill crawling up my spine was from the cell door or the cold aluminum. Either way, I was not happy.

"How much time do you need?" inquired Sergeant Atkins.

"About an hour," I replied.

I motioned for Harjoe to join me at the dinner table. He crept toward me and sat gingerly on the bench. The five other inmates peered at me while I stared at Harjoe. I didn't want to make eye contact with the other inmates because eye contact would solicit unwanted conversations. However, contact or not, a small in stature but large in voice man came over to greet me.

"My name is Stan Beene from Utah."

I nodded at him out of politeness.

"I was just passing through your great state and got busted. The drugs weren't mine, and I'm going ape shit in here and ... " Utah Stan amused the other inmates, who were probably relieved that he had someone new to explain his interstate troubles to.

"Mr. Beene! Mr. Beene! It is nice to meet you. It isn't my intention to be unfriendly, but I have only an hour to interview Mr. Harjoe," I said.

"Oh that's all right. I think if you hear my problem, then you'll want to set things straight where I can get back to Utah and see my five children and take care of my dying mother. My brother is also sick, but he is in the state penitentiary. I can't get on his visitor's list 'cause I'm on probation for stealing chickens. Did I mention I'm going 'ape shit?"

"Mr. Beene ... please, let me do this interview, and if I still have some time we can visit." I knew the interview would take every second of an hour, and if it didn't I would make sure it did, but I had to offer Utah Stan something.

"Sure, that'll work. Man, you're all right. Just let me know when you're ready. I'll be right over here reading this book, *Valley Of The Dolls*. Have you heard of it? It's pretty good. I read *Old Yeller* last week, and I found similarities in both books." Utah Stan walked away with his book, and I started to explain the interview process to Harjoe.

From Harjoe's appearance and mannerisms I anticipated a laid back attitude, which would make Harjoe dodge questions and forget answers. I thought the interview would be difficult and the hour wouldn't be long enough. However, I was pleasantly surprised. He spoke with thought and anticipation. Furthermore, he didn't volunteer information or encourage Utah Stan. Even though he didn't tell me, I believed he welcomed the interruption of his daily jail routine.

Harjoe liked for me to call him by his full name: Kevin Faye Harjoe. His mother was from Mexico, and his father was half Kiowa Indian and half African American. Faye was his mother's first name. "That's an unusual blood line," I told him.

"Yelp."

I was glad that I didn't need to make small talk.

He had graduated high school and even attempted several classes at two junior colleges. His criminal record started when he was about 20. Either he became a criminal at 20 or he started getting caught at 20. It was hard to tell. His previous felony convictions included Concealing Stolen Property, Distribution of a Controlled Dangerous Substance, and a misdemeanor conviction for Possession of Marijuana. Now, at the age of 29, he was charged with Possession of a Controlled Dangerous Substance with the Intent to Distribute.

Despite all of his convictions, he had never served prison time. The first felony resulted in a deferred sentence that was expunged after two years of supervision. On the second felony offense, he received five years suspended. The probation sentence included 100 hours of community service and a $5,000 fine. Harjoe explained how the current charge was the result of money he owed to a loan shark for paying off the fine on the suspended sentence. The loan shark made Harjoe sell drugs, which the shark considered a form of community service. He couldn't remember the interest rate but guaranteed me triple digit interest was a possibility.

The interview sailed from one question to another. Since Utah Stan kept smiling at me and since I didn't want to chat with him, I asked several questions from the Client Management Classification Assessment Interview process, also know as the CMC. I used the CMC, a motivational interview process, to place clients in one of several behavioral categories. Before I could finish the CMC questions, an inmate in the far right corner of the cell started yelling.

"I'm a Casework Control," Utah Stan proudly announced. This proclamation certainly told me a lot. Case Work Control is one of the classification categories and it indicated that Mr. Beene needed to be closely monitored on the streets. I thanked him for his interjection and focused my attention on Mr. Harjoe.

After Utah Stan settled down, I wrapped up the interview and summarized Harjoe's responses. I was glad I wouldn't be writing the pre-sentence report because a recommendation to the court or even a case plan would be difficult. Harjoe didn't feel victimized by his environment or his life, and he was intelligent. He didn't appear to have a drug problem and admitted to selling drugs as his sole source of income. He made no excuses for his behavior and, as a matter of fact, he may have been the first "guilty" offender I ever interviewed.

I thanked Harjoe for the interview and kept one eye on Utah Stan. Stan was busy in a heated card game of Texas Hold 'Em with the remainder of the Cell Block Six. Time had flown by, and my watch indicated an hour and a half had passed. Since I knew an officer would soon return, I walked to the door with the same command performance in which I entered. Only this time, I gripped the bars and waited.

I looked right and then left. No sign of Sergeant Atkins or any other officer. No footsteps coming down the hallway; nothing but the noise of Utah Stan and the others playing cards. I could hear the cards shuffling and Stan mumbling "cheater" under his breath. When no one noticed his "cheater" comment, he referred to himself as the "Bantam Rooster" and made references to his fighting abilities and chickens.

Waiting several minutes, I heard a faint sound coming down the corridor. My knuckles turned white from gripping the bars as I tried to stick my neck through the metal openings. Harjoe mimicked my actions.

"That's just Rocky snoring in cell eight. Sounds kind of like a freight train or an elevator."

Harjoe offered to throw a set of dominoes down the hall to wake up Rocky, which he thought would be very entertaining, but I refused. I thanked him for the information and returned to my perch.

At 8 p.m. the card game was over and I was still standing near the bars. I was anxious, but panic was still in the distance. Harjoe occasionally walked to the front of the cell while Utah Stan quoted *Old Yeller*. The seconds turned into minutes and the minutes into another hour. I removed my hands from the bars when I realized my knuckles were now white and blood red. Harjoe sensed my annoyance and frustration.

"Hey man, it's not unusual for us not see anyone on the late shift, unless of course if someone been acting crazy all day. Then officers come by every half hour. There was too much watching when the county employees ran this place and sometimes not enough with the private companies here. When all is well we don't need them walking this floor all the time but when things aren't well, well, you get the point."

With the support of several cell mates, Harjoe continued. "The food is better now but less of it. Public service and increasing earnings don't always mix." Harjoe's editorial certainly distracted me whether he intended for it to or not.

When Harjoe's explanation was over, I began to pace back and forth. "I told him one hour," I muttered. Before Officer Atkins left, he told me to be patient with the situation. "Patience my ass," I rambled. "Patience my ass..." I'd had enough patience for one night. I didn't even break stride when Harjoe suggested I was acting like an inmate. I didn't care. I wanted out, and I wanted to go now! To make things worse, Utah Stan, tired of playing poker, started hanging from the bars.

"I'm going ape shit," he yelled and pointed at me. "He's going ape shit." I thought I was going ape shit because I was contemplating what the hell ape shit meant. I did not want to be in a cage. I wanted to be alone and plan my revenge. Whatever I could devise, I knew Jason had it coming.

10:00 p.m. ... Surely my wife was looking for me ... The office would be closed but maybe she could contact one of the officers who saw me leave ... They would know that I was headed towards the county jail ... I prayed she hadn't started calling hospitals or the police station ... Surely, Sergeant Atkins didn't forget me ... He must have remembered me in the shift change ... He simply couldn't have forgotten about me.

What if I have to spend the night here? What if my cell mates became unfriendly? What if I was dreaming and couldn't wake up? What if I *was* going ape shit? I couldn't stay there and play cards with my cellmates.

> ### What should I have done?
> A. Convince my cellmates to grease up Utah Stan, squeeze him through the bars, and send him for help.
> A. Organize an escape attempt.
> B. Start a fire to set off the smoke alarms.
> C. Throw dominoes down the hall to wake up Rocky, and start a verbal exchange of hostilities. Maybe the noise would bring a jailer.
> D. Be a professional, lie down, and do my time.

Since the thought of staying the night in this cell was despicable, I started pacing across the whole room. I moved from each corner into the others until I had completed a square. The inmates, except for Harjoe and Utah Stan, turned in for the night. Harjoe and Utah Stan offered me their bunks, but I refused. They understood why I couldn't sleep in this cell, and I continued my walk.

"Ain't this the shits," remarked Utah Stan. "You know you ain't getting out of here tonight. It's a damn conspiracy. It's just another damn way to keep me from going home to Utah."

I was curious about how in the hell this was a conspiracy and what did me spending the night in jail have to do with him going home? I rolled my eyes and decided not to ask. Harjoe and I sat at the picnic table, discussed his future, and, of course, ignored Utah Stan.

Midnight and all was well. At least that was what I was trying to convince myself. Utah Stan was now asleep with his head resting on his folded arms stretched across the picnic table. Harjoe's eyes appeared heavy, but he was committed to my cause. Harjoe was going to stay the course until I was paroled. I dozed off until I heard the familiar sound of the elevator. Harjoe and I raced toward the bars and bent our necks to where we could see the reflection of the elevator in the shiny waxed floors. I heard footsteps...Polished footsteps.

"Officer, down here!" I yelled and woke up Utah Stan.

"Hey man, we got a parole officer down here!" Harjoe bellowed.

"Going ape shit down here!" Utah Stan shouted.

Cautious steps approached with the methodical rhythm of a drum major on downers. I thought the officer would never arrive. He stopped to talk to Rocky, who was complaining that some asshole threw dominoes at him. Harjoe laughed.

Finally, the officer arrived with his starched blue uniform and polished military dress shoes. He wore a two-inch wide black tie and an Al Franken fondue haircut. He turned to face us as if he were a part of the changing of the guards. I stared at this robotic man with a victimized face and a "get me the hell out of here" attitude. Harjoe remained cool, and Utah Stan balanced on one foot.

"Gentlemen, it is lights out, and you need to step away from the bars and bunk down for the night." Harjoe either had encountered this officer before or he had enough street sense to step away from the bars. However, I needed to make my escape. "Officer, I'm glad you are here. I was beginning to think Sergeant Atkins had forgotten about me. I'm finished and I'm ready to go home now. I bet my wife is either worried sick about my whereabouts or is mad as hell."

"Stop right there young man. First of all you need to back away from those bars if you wish to speak to me. I glanced over my shoulder and saw Harjoe leaning against the back wall of the cell. He motioned with his eyes for me to step back. "That's better," the officer said. Then the order came again, "Time to bunk down."

"I guess Sergeant Atkins didn't tell you who I am or why I'm here?" I enquired.

"Well, I guess he didn't, and I suspect you are going to tell me?"

"I am," I responded in the most respectful tone of voice I could conjure, but it wasn't respectful enough.

"Young man, if you want to stay in this cell with your buddies and not get moved to lock up, you had better watch your sarcasm."

I wanted to yell "I am a probation officer! Get me out of here!" but didn't think he would believe me. I squinted my eyes to read the officers name tag, so I could address him in a more respectful and courteous manner. Officer Kahn. My first thought was "Shit, I'm going to reason with a great, great, great, great grandson of an infamous Mongolian King."

"Officer Kahn, I am a probation officer."

Before I could finish, Officer Kahn smiled and said, "You know we get all kinds. Last week we had a lawyer in here for killing his wife's boyfriend. What you in for young man?"

"You don't understand," I started talking faster. "I haven't committed any crime. I was in here interviewing Ha…"

Again before I could finish my sentence Officer Kahn interrupted. "You guys are all innocent. If I had a dime for every innocent inmate that came through here, then I could buy out Bill Gates." Now I knew what Utah Stan meant when he said he was going ape shit. I saw my future as a chicken thief, and it did not look pretty.

"I *am* a probation officer! I was interviewing Harjoe, and Sergeant Atkins was supposed to return and let me out in an hour." Harjoe softly approached where I stood and had a smile like the cat from *Alice in Wonderland.*

"You don't look like a probation officer. Probation officers don't wear jeans and polo shirts. You must be special."

With a frustrated but helpless look, I turned to Harjoe for help.

Harjoe was about to speak, but Utah Stan interrupted. "He ain't no probation officer, and if he is then I'm George W. Bush." This was his way of getting back at me for ignoring him most of the evening. Harjoe cut his eyes toward Utah Stan and he didn't say another word. He curled up his thin, feeble face and went back to bed.

"Officer, this man is telling the truth. He really is a probation officer. I don't know what happened to Sergeant Atkins, but we've been waiting for someone to let Officer Reeves out," explained Harjoe.

"You got any identification?" Officer Kahn requested. I knew it would come to this. I was going to have to explain the bureau's casual day, my forgotten identification, Jason's sneaky speech, and my predicament. So I did. I explained the whole mess to Officer Kahn.

"I'm sorry son. You're going to have to do better than that." A platoon of butterflies prepared for battle in my stomach. I motioned to Harjoe for assistance, but he only turned and walked towards his bunk. I gave up. As I mentally prepared a lawsuit and planned to let Officer Kahn deal with my wife, a huge smile crept across his stoic face.

"Come on now Officer Reeves, you can't blame a fellow for having a little fun on the graveyard shift. Walking these halls can get a little boring at times." If I could have strangled him through the bars, I would have. "I know who you are. Sergeant Atkins called a few minutes ago. Seems he forgot to tell me about you at shift change. He says to tell you he is real sorry and a little extra time in the stir probably did you good."

I was conflicted. I felt relief, I felt embarrassed, and I wanted to whoop some ass. When I saw the key go into the lock and heard the sound of the cylinder turning, my conflicts disappeared. I was ecstatic! I was free at last, and my wife was going to kill me.

I thanked Officer Kahn and said goodbye to Harjoe. "No hard feelings?" asked Officer Kahn.

"No hard feelings" I replied.

Officer Kahn winked at Harjoe, and Harjoe smiled. At that moment, I realized he had been in on it. I must have missed Kahn's wink when he first approached the cell, but I had certainly caught this one. I said nothing.

As I exited the cell, Harjoe told me to be "cool" and to stay out of jail. He also advised me to stay in school and to not do drugs. "Thanks man for helping on my pre-sentence when you could've been off." This time I smiled and left the cell.

Officer Kahn and I almost made it to the elevator before Utah Stan shouted, "I was just jokin'! I was jokin'! Take me with you! I need to get to Utah. I'm a probation officer too. I'm undercover!" The closing elevator doors silenced Stan's pleading.

I walked outside the jail toward the parking lot, looked up at the harvest moon, and filled my lungs with the crisp autumn air. The midnight breeze moved the leaves around my feet as I approached my dear Chevette. I fumbled around trying to find my keys and watched a woman get out of the only other car in the parking lot. She glowed in the moonlight but was not too happy to see me.

"Sweetheart," I said. "Sugar, I'm sorry for being late." Her arms were folded across her chest, legs crossed at the ankles.

"You could have called. I called hospitals. I called the police. Then I found your duty officer number, and lucky for you the duty officer saw you leaving the office to come down here. Why in the hell did it take so long?" she questioned.

I thought long and hard for a good answer. I had run the gauntlet of emotions this evening and I just wasn't sure if I could withstand providing a lengthy explanation.

"Honey," I shook my head out of embarrassment and frustration. "Honey, it was ape shit in there. Let's go get a couple of margaritas at Garcia's, and I'll tell you all about it."

Chapter Four
"Momma's Family"

"Don't call my mother a bitch! If you say it again, I'll kick your ass!" Bobby Glass tried to jump and wiggle towards me, but the handcuffs and Jake kept him fastened to his chair.

We used to have a wonderful receptionist who would have side-tracked this confrontation by tackling his mother to the ground before letting her run into my office, but the receptionist retired last week. The budget cuts left the front desk vacant and my office susceptible to the violence of Bobby's mother. A receptionist well-trained in the science of offenders and family behaviors would have seen this wreck coming.

But I am getting ahead of myself ... let me first give you some background information.

Bobby Glass was an absconder, a community supervised offender who failed to report for an extended period of time and who had no intention of returning to the judicial system. Often absconders move without noting a forwarding address or leave the state without obtaining permission. I had tried to keep Bobby from absconding. I often contacted former girlfriends, past employers, utility companies, and, when all else failed, his mom.

When I would finally find him, Bobby was always glad to see me. It was a little game to him. We would meet and review the importance of reporting and paying court imposed financial obligations, or we would have our usual chat about responsibility. He would simply smile through each of my speeches because his cognitive abilities kept him from understanding his predicament. His mentality and his heated temper (Jake and I called him "hothead") created extreme conflict between Bobby and others around him, both his officers and his family. Bobby and his family had an unbalanced love-hate relationship.

At times, I felt like I was supervising his whole family. He had an on again, off again scenario with his estranged wife and repeated problems with his girlfriends. Bobby would call on Fridays to complain about his wife, on Tuesdays to talk about his girlfriend, and on Thursdays to vent about his mother.

However, I never knew where he was. His wife would call once a week to gripe about his behavior and domestic violence. Sometimes, when Bobby reported, his black eyes, scratches, and bruises told me that he had lost some part of the battle with his wife. When I saw his wife, it looked like a split decision.

In any case, I was constantly refereeing and referring. I conducted collateral contacts and talked to every human resource agency in the county. After two years of attempting to save him from revocation, my probation and parole officer skills were exhausted, and I had finally run out of patience with Bobby. He had failed to report for three months, and this time, in lieu of my usual routine of finding him and holding his hand through reporting, I wrote a violation report to the court declaring him the worst of all probation sins: an absconder.

After I had submitted the violation report, our district attorney issued a revocation warrant. He didn't like Bobby and was waiting for him to screw up. Once the warrant was activated, I visited Bobby's mother once a month. Each time she would come to the door, scream obscenities, and tell me she hadn't seen Bobby.

On one occasion, she grabbed her curling iron and waved it around like a sword. She referred to my visits as "harassment" and an "invasion of privacy" and believed the law would be on her side. Also, she threatened to call the police or Judge Judy if I bothered her again. I always kept my cool, remembering that I was just doing my job. I never told her that there was an outstanding warrant for Bobby's arrest because the information would create a longer hunt for Bobby, not to mention the wrath of this domestic Medusa.

When Bobby finally called the office, I admonished him for his failure to report and told him to come into the bureau later that afternoon. He responded with uncontrolled indignation. He stated that he was living with a new girlfriend and working as a rough neck in an oil field. In addition, he wanted to know why I hadn't found him.

He was like a child playing hide-and-go-seek; I had lost. Normally, winning made Bobby happy, but since I hadn't spent hours looking for him, the game became a failure. I made arrangements for him to come to the office, but I didn't tell him about the warrant or the encounters with his mom. Since I needed help detaining Bobby, I turned to my office partner, Jake Pratt.

Jake started his career a year before me, but as he reminded me daily, the year made *him* the expert. When I received my five-year longevity pin last April at The Red Rooster, I started considering Jake and me as senior officers, but as Jake would tell me, he was the "professional."

Jake was a tall, slow talking and walking man. He swayed back and forth when he moseyed and mumbled when he told jokes. He was one of the officers I trusted because he was always there for me.

When we went absconder hunting – Jake's favorite past time and answer to any situation – his black belt in karate came in handy. After our last absconder hunt, Jake tried to teach me karate, but I fell flat on my face. He picked me up and, of course, told the entire office.

He was my beloved best friend, and the best absconder catcher I had ever seen. I explained the situation to Jake, who had heard me complain about Bobby before. We decided to use our favorite procedure, the chair arrest. Jake planned to observe my conversation with Bobby and wait for the appropriate cue.

When Bobby arrived, he had his new girlfriend in tow. She looked a lot like his wife: tiny, conservatively dressed, no make up, and stringy unkempt hair. His girlfriend, like her predecessors, had low-self esteem and let Bobby pick out her attire. She wore a loose, flowery dress that hid her figure and cowgirl boots that smelled of hard labor. Bobby looked like he always did: customary sleeveless under shirt – torn, tattered, and tucked into dirty 501 Levy Jeans. He wore steel-toed work shoes and a blue bandana holding back his shoulder length hair. He was happy to see me, and he tried to keep a playful attitude when he introduced his girlfriend.

"This is my chick, Nicky." He smiled and pointed. He sat in the chair closest to my desk; she stood by his side. Bobby seemed relaxed and appreciative that once again I had given him a break.

I began the conversation with the importance of following the rules of probation, slowly outlining his unacceptable conduct. I then relayed a discussion I had with the district attorney about Bobby's failure to report. At the conclusion of the speech, I made a casual remark about the warrant and stated, "Oh by the way, you are under arrest."

His girlfriend jumped towards the door, expecting a violent reaction from him; however, Bobby remained calm. After reading him his Miranda rights, I told him to place his hands behind the chair. Jake handcuffed Bobby before Bobby even knew where he was placing his hands.

Bobby tried to reach for his now crying girlfriend, but Jake kept his foot planted over the rung of the chair. While I handed Nicky a box of tissues that

I kept for just such occasions, I explained to Bobby that the judge and DA would have the final say in the revocation process and I would be asked for a recommendation. I advised him my comments would depend on his cooperation. Since Bobby was also behind on court costs and restitution payments, Nicky wrote down the total delinquent amount and asked to use the phone in the hallway.

Jake and I were set to go. Bobby was firmly secured in the chair, and the sobbing girlfriend had left. I called the police for a transport to the county jail, and Jake continued to stand watch over our captive absconder. Since we had lost one detainee before and were determined to never lose another one, we kept all four eyes on Bobby. Jake and I sat around, talking about the time the offender got away and wondering where the girlfriend had gone.

"Jake this was an easy catch." I said.

"Yelp," Jake mumbled.

"I was looking for a little action," I yawned, "but I'm glad it's over."

As the expert, Jake couldn't let me gloat about the situation. He had to offer a few words of advice.

"Jack, whatever you do, never, ever, think the arrest is over until custody is transferred to another agency because all hell could break loose."

I stood there for a moment, tapping my fingers on my desk, thinking Jake was a smart ass, and wondering when the police would show up. I was proud of myself and happy that I didn't have to see Bobby or his mother again anytime soon.

How the mother from hell got to the office before Bobby's transport remains a mystery. Before I could retaliate to Jake's comment, she stood in my doorway with her hands on her hips, hunched over like a Green Bay Packer ready to tackle the Cowboys' quarterback. She had arms as big as a football player's, but no muscle at all. She was ranting something about how Nicky should have called her sooner.

When she put her hands on her hips, the skin on her underarm and the cigarette stuck to her bottom lip both jiggled. She smelled like Shasta and hair spray. She had the classic white-bleached blonde hair ratted into the shape of an exploding atomic bomb. White makeup was strategically caked on her nose and chin in an attempt to minimize the acreage of her face. Her mascara had produced eyelashes that were long and wide, and her eye shadow was toilet bowl blue. Last time I saw her, she had eye brows. Now they had been plucked into oblivion and replaced with two, one-inch wide slashes of black magic marker. She stood behind Jake, blocking the doorway and our exit.

"What in the hell are you doing with my boy?!" she screamed in a voice so shrill, pigeons having their breakfast outside my window choked and ran. They were so scared that they forgot how to fly.

"Ms. Glass, be calm," I suggested. She ignored me and gave Jake an evil look.

"You aren't taking my son to jail! Bobby get up and let's get out of here," she demanded. Bobby looked a little bewildered and confused.

"I said let's go Bobby!"

Bobby started to stand, but Jake, possessor of the black belt, placed his hands firmly on Bobby's shoulders and responded. "Ms. Glass, you are going to have to calm down, or I am going to force you to leave. Bobby is going to jail."

"You're not taking my *boy* to prison. Come on Bobby, let's go!" Again, Jake prevented Bobby's escape.

I couldn't take it any longer. I had to talk to this woman.

"Ms. Glass, we're waiting on the police, and you're coming real close to interfering with this arrest. I strongly suggest you have a seat and calm down. You can wait with us and can meet Bobby at the jail."

Jake motioned to the unoccupied chair in my office, but Ms. Glass didn't accept the invitation. She stepped into the office and assumed the space the girlfriend once occupied. Nicky had never returned from the phone call, and it was a mistake on our part to allow her to leave. We were the only two in the office and for all we knew she could have been retrieving a weapon from her car. Jake and I were feeling the effects of rapidly increasing adrenalin. We were on high alert.

"Bobby, this man has been harassing me for months. He comes by the trailer at all hours of the night, wakes me up, and treats me like a criminal. He's rude and accused me of lying!" Momma cried out. Bobby's angry face turned towards me.

"I am many things, ma'am, but I'm not a liar." I could feel the muscles in my face clench. "I have never accused you of anything. I was only looking for your son, Bobby," I explained.

"You're a liar, and I'll sue your ass! My son has done nothing wrong! You make me sick!"

With these accusations, Bobby's mom took a step towards me. She lifted her over sized finger and started waving it in my face. She jerked her head back and forth while her volume increased. One more step and I could have smoked her cigarette. I placed the palms of my hands outward, displaying the universal sign for stop.

"Don't point your finger at me you son of a bitch!" she screamed while reaching out in an attempt to push my hands aside.

She grabbed my hands, and I could no longer hear her babbling. My senses went into warp speed. She raised her hand to slap me. I grabbed Momma by both wrists and attempted a defensive move. At that moment, Bobby decided to come to his mother's rescue. He pushed the chair into Jake and lunged for his mother. Jake quickly defeated Bobby and secured him with a martial arts choke hold. While Bobby gasped for air, finally signaled he had had enough and his face returned to its normal hue.

Mommy dearest didn't struggle nor did she scream for help; however, she did conjure a stream of obscenities of which the devil would have been ashamed. Jake called for an exorcist.

Somewhere in this barrage of obscure sailor jargon, I lost my cool. I blurted out an unconscious phrase, "Bitch, sit down!"

In that moment, maybe just maybe, I lost my professionalism. Whatever the phrase and no matter the consequence, my demand did the trick. The fountain of obscenities, the old faithful of trash talk, shut up.

"Don't call my mother a bitch! If you say it again, I'll kick your ass!" Bobby Glass tried to jump and wiggle towards me, but the handcuffs and Jake kept him fastened to his chair.

"I did not call your mother a bitch!"

"Yes you did!"

Bobby was right. I did call her a bitch. The room transformed into Madam Trusso's House of Wax with no one moving, not even Momma. Jake looked at me in shock and slowly formed a smirk on his face. Still holding Momma's hands, I wasn't sure what I should do next.

Should I have:
A. Thrown Momma to the ground and handcuffed her.
B. Kisses her hand and beg for forgiveness.
C. Pointed to Jake and said, "He said it."
D. Regained my composure and apologized.
E. Said nothing and proceeded with the arrest.

Descending from warp speed, I relaxed my grip on momma's wrists. Bobby glared at me and Jake smirked. We had worked together long enough for me to read his thoughts. He knew I had screwed up, and I knew he would never allow me to live it down.

Regaining my composure and controlling the situation, I said, "Ms. Glass, I am going to let go of your wrists now. When I do, I am asking you nicely to step back into the hallway. If not, I'll place you under arrest. I apologize for calling you a bitch. If you have issues with me, I suggest you take them elsewhere." Wiping much of her eye brow off with her hand, she did as I requested.

"I'm suing your ass!" she informed me while backing into the hallway.

"That is your prerogative," I conceded.

Once the situation was secure, Police Officer Combs arrived on the scene. His uniform commanded the attention of all and even Momma didn't speak. I handed a copy of the warrant to Officer Combs while Jake explained that due to matters beyond our control a search of the arrestee hadn't been conducted. Just when the environment felt normal again, Momma dearest, the symbol of maternal domesticity, re-emerged with a vengeance.

"This son of a bitch called me a bitch and has been harassing me!" she ranted. "I'm going to sue his ass and yours too if you take my son to jail on this illegal warrant."

"Madam, please step aside. Tell your complaints to the judge," Officer Combs instructed.

"I'm telling you right now. Ain't you supposed to uphold the law? I want to file a complaint," she demanded, pointing at me and holding her wrists.

"Madam, I've advised you what to do, and I strongly suggest you do it." Momma held her ground and made no effort to step aside. Bobby wanted the situation to end.

"Momma, it's okay. Go get some bail money. It'll be okay."

"No. It ain't going to be all right until these assholes recognize my rights."

Officer Combs passed Bobby back to Jake and asked momma to turn around. As momma was loading her mouth with new unadulterated profanity, Officer Combs took her arms and quickly placed handcuffs on each wrist.

"You can't do this!" momma screamed. "I know my rights." Jake and I expected Bobby to react but no resistance occurred. His mother's actions genuinely embarrassed him.

"You are under arrest for interfering in the lawful arrest of another," Officer Combs explained to the indignant mother.

She slung another ribbon of obscenities so foul even I was impressed. Officer Combs called for another patrol car and in minutes they were joyfully on their way to the county jail. Jake and I waved goodbye to Bobby and ignored Momma's yelling.

Calling this woman a bitch offended my belief system. I shouldn't have lost my control. In repentance, I confessed my sin to my supervisor. Jake dialed the phone and waited to listen to the conference call. "Yes, ma'am, I indeed called this woman a bitch, and I have witnesses." I groveled for awhile before my boss passed sentence.

"If you do it again, you are fired," she said. As my stomach tied into a sailor's knot, I sank in my chair.

"Better yet," she bellowed, "I aught to fire you right now!" I thought I was going to throw up.

Jake started to laugh.

"Jack, are you still there?" She questioned.

"Yes, ma'am. I'm still listening."

"You're gullible Jack," she chuckled. "Officer Jack Pruitt, if that is the worst thing you ever do as an officer, you'll be lucky," advised my boss.

"Thank you ma'am ... You have a great sense of humor." I said as I ended the call.

I turned to Jake, not exactly sure what had just happened. "She really was joking, right?"

About sixty days later I was in court for Bobby's graduation from a probationer to an inmate. Jake had come along for the entertainment. Once I took the witness stand, my heart softened. When the judge asked me what I recommended, I suggested credit for time served and another opportunity at finishing his probation sentence. The judge and prosecutor agreed.

As I was leaving the court house, Bobby's mother was walking up the steps. There was no possible way to avoid her, or I would have. As we passed, I distinctly heard her say, "Thanks you son of a bitch for my week in the county jail."

Then I thought, "What've I done?" But it was too late to find the judge and advise him I had changed my mind. The thought of having to make home visits and seeing this woman made me want to quit and become a social worker or something like that.

Jake could tell the trauma of the revocation hearing and now the pleasant good morning from Momma had ruined my day.

"Hey Jack, it's a beautiful fall morning. We can't go back to the office on a day like today. This is an ideal field day."

"Shut up, Jake."

He ignored me and continued to be giddy. I couldn't help but laugh. "What should we do?" I asked.

"Let's go absconder hunting."

Chapter Five
"The Council"

Jake and I had the choice to return to office work or continue to do field work. The day beckoned us to field work. We had just dealt with one absconder, and there were many more to locate. We decided we would go back to the office to gather the necessary paper work. We would search first for some of Jake's absconders, and then some of mine.

When we arrived at the office, an irate offender was complaining to our new rookie officer about how inappropriate it was for her to make a field contact at his house. He explained that her presence made his wife jealous. Jake and I stood in the doorway just in case we were needed to calm the situation. Ms. Harris, our rookie, tapped her pen on the side of her desk until the offender finished his complaint. He paused to breath and she motioned for him to take a seat. She refused to sit, standing directly over her client.

"Get over it! Deal with it," she stated in a controlled yet booming voice. "You're on probation, not me," she pointed her long red fingernail at his crooked grimace. "And I will come by your house as needed. I suspect it is you who has the problem with me coming to your house, not your wife."

The young man sat speechless. Apparently he had grossly underestimated the tenacity of Ms. Harris. Before Jake and I continued down the hall, the offender was saying "Yes, Ms. Harris" and "No, Ms. Harris." We mocked his child-like responses as we walked down the corridor. I probably would have addressed the situation differently and with less confrontation, but I couldn't criticize her approach. I only wish Ms. Harris and Bobby's mother could have met.

We gathered our absconder files to determine who we would try to locate.

If we suspected an absconder was out of state, then a phone call to the last address would count as an attempt to locate. Sometimes phone calls to relatives, ex-spouses, children, or friends would uncover an absconder's whereabouts, and then we would venture for a field attempt. Also, the obituary notices and accident reports sometimes helped us locate our absconders.

Apart from our direct attempts to locate absconders, we always maintained current rap sheets. We couldn't afford to look for an absconder all day only to find out later that the offender was already in jail. Sometimes we saw one of our clients on the front page of the newspaper or on the evening news for performing a heinous crime. The possibility of an absconder committing a new crime required us to keep our files in good order and stay up to date on locater attempts. If not, there would be hell to pay.

For Jake and me, absconder hunting was both a science and an art, consisting of one part sociology, psychology, anthropology, and luck and two parts probation officer instinct. We were a Midwest Scotland Yard. The sciences enabled us to understand the various societies our offenders lived in and how our actions could affect our success. We needed to know where our clients came from and the culture in which they resided.

Our intuition told us if a spouse or friend was lying or misdirecting our trail. In order to secure a location, we observed keenly and assessed wisely all the bit players and the environmental characteristics. With a little luck the arrest would go smoothly. Our methods changed absconder hunting from a concrete probation officer task into an artistic endeavor.

Twice a year Jake taught absconder hunting at the training academy and on several occasions, we located persons when the police could not. Many times our office and local law enforcement personnel would be searching for the same desperado. To show our camaraderie, Jake and I would start a contest with a couple of the detectives to see who could find the absconder first. Of course, we always won the prize: a greasy, onion cheese burger, fries, and a watered-down coke at the Town and Country Grill.

The fun was in the game and hunt, not necessarily the capture. So, on this beautiful fall morning, we were about to embark on Jake's favorite sporting event, absconder hunting. We gathered our files, and my mouth watered for the caramelized onions and side of fried potatoes.

Jake and I said our goodbyes to Officer Harris and also bid farewell in a "glad I'm not you" tone to her wayward offender. I took the wheel of our luxurious hand-me-down agency car: a totally refurbished 1983 Chevrolet Citation. Jake refused to turn the air conditioner on because he wanted to enjoy the morning breeze. After we stopped by the county sheriff's office to verify the sixteen warrants for our absconders, we returned to the beautiful weather and our long awaited day of field work.

The morning was indeed pristine – not a cloud in the sky, and a slight breeze meandered from the southwest. An Indian summer, Jake called it. The temperature peaked at about 65 degrees, and we drove the state car with the windows down. I couldn't think of a better atmosphere in which to go knocking on doors, climbing in and out of cars, walking around apartment complexes, and driving through the country.

I needed the few hours of relative freedom. I was glad the whole episode with Bobby Glass and his mother was over. Well, it wasn't really over. I still had to figure out how to do office and field contacts without having altercations with Mommy Dearest, but I ignored that situation for the moment and was contently entranced as I stared at the staccato white lines flying toward me like tracer rounds.

On my caseload, several offenders had absconded from the first day they were sentenced to probation. I had inherited most of these road warriors from former or transferred officers. For some of my cases, depending on who made the initial arrest, resulting in a conviction and subsequent probation, there were no photographs available. These absconders had become legend. Jake and I would casually comment about them over our onion burgers after finding an absconder and winning the bet with the local law enforcement. "Maybe our waiter is one of them," Jake would joke.

"Maybe ... Why don't you put a Chinese choke hold on him so that we can find out?" We'd have a good laugh and return to our meal of chili fries and coke.

Geographical boundaries divided my caseload from other probation officer caseloads. However, false addresses or unbalanced workloads between officers could make my caseload overlap with another officer's jurisdiction. The year before, I had inherited the most rural area of our supervision districts because of an overlap. The former officer needed a break from traveling, and I needed the field experience.

Now, I wanted a break from the large caseload. I had nearly 150 clients, twenty-five more than the previous officer. Also, many of my offenders resided at least 50 miles from the nearest town, and my clients tended to live an hour or more from any other offender on my caseload. Jake thought my carping over work was quite humorous. All of his offenders were concentrated within the city limits and a majority of them lived in a particular area of town. Four or five even lived in the same apartment complex.

Before we ventured out of town, we made a few stops to find offenders on Jake's caseload. He made notes from contacts who were collaterally related to the case and developed several reliable leads on two absconders. One grandmother of an absconder praised us for our efforts and wished us good luck in our endeavor. She wanted us to capture her grandson before he got into more trouble or before someone killed him. She thought he was doing drugs and knew we could save him. Another collateral contact, a mother, made it clear that we forced her son to run away. She believed our harassment, demands, and fee collections scared her son, and he had no other choice but to leave.

She didn't understand that many clients led Jake and me to be one of two characters. Either we were the evil probation enforcer who made clients meet with us (possibly the most unpleasant experience of their lives) and comply with court orders or we were the helpers who supported and assisted our clients, helped them to become more pro-social and law-abiding. Since there were many attitudes we could take and several hats we could wear, sometimes choosing the wrong representation made the job difficult. However, today the only persona we wanted to portray was absconder hunters extraordinaire. No other personality would do.

The morning's activities and the afternoon's adventures – paired with the fact that we had missed lunch – forced us to stop for refreshments at a small country store, fifty miles from the city and twenty miles from the nearest gas station. We always stopped at the same store because it was the only store in the area. Its location made it an oasis for our growling stomachs as well as a barrel-full of local gossip. The owner recognized everyone in the area and always knew who we were looking for.

On this sunny mid-afternoon, Jake and I sat on an old oak bench on the store's front porch. Only the breeze kissing the tumbleweeds and the fizz from my soda broke the silence of the old convenience store. The air began to turn colder, and when I leaned back on the old tin RC Cola sign converted to a bench back, chills ran down my spine. I tossed the cap from my glass soda bottle into the millions of round tin lids reflecting the sun in the parking lot. I squinted, trying to read many of the brands I never heard of.

"I didn't even know they still made glass bottles." I told Jake.

"They probably don't. I think this bottle is from 1955."

The leaves falling off the only tree matched the brown rustic exterior of the store. Mr. Biles, the owner, claimed that the store had never been painted and that he would never bother to paint. "I'm into nostalgia. It's looked this way since I was little, and it'll look this way 'til I die."

He stood on the porch and asked if we needed anything else because he was going to close for the day. 3 p.m. He didn't expect to have anymore customers for the rest of the day. "Ya see, the farmers only come in the mornin' ... bright'n early." He handed us a complimentary piece of taffy and locked the front door.

"Mr. Biles, you haven't seen Kyle Beavers around here lately?" I inquired. I had asked this particular question every month for the past year.

The answer in some form or fashion was always the same...this time was no different, "Can't say that I have. Haven't seen that boy in years. You know he come into a lot of money when his daddy died, and he sold the mineral rights to that there oil company. With that kinda money, he won't be comin' around here. His daddy's ol' place just sets there rottin' away."

Kyle Beavers was one of those absconders I had never seen nor did I have any photos of him. He absconded moments after receiving his suspended sentence. No intake interview was ever conducted. From contacts with relatives and local law enforcement, I developed some profile information on Kyle.

He was Native American with heritage from three tribes: Kiowa, Apache and Comanche. One of his aunts told me Kyle claimed only his Apache heritage. He felt that the Apaches exemplified his beliefs. He was known to be extremely intelligent but quit school in the ninth grade. The principal told me he celebrated the day Kyle decided that school wasn't for him.

The local group of young Apaches admired his leadership and claimed he was honest and giving; however, they couldn't give me a proper identification of him. On paper, he had five DUI (Driving While Under the Influence of Intoxicating Liquor) convictions; the last two were filed as felony cases that had resulted in his five-year suspended sentence and placed him under probation supervision.

I thanked Mr. Biles for his hospitality. He mentioned something about never seeing us unless it was a beautiful day and said he looked forward to visiting with us next month. Jake and I nodded in agreement, thanked him for the taffy, and returned to our car. Mr. Biles knew our pattern. We were no different than uniformed law enforcement who gave out more speeding tickets on nice days than on rainy days.

With the all important contact attempt in mind, I sped past the repetitive telephone poles and solitary silos of the plains. I was motivated by a lot of things. The client contact attempt fed the agency count, and the agency count was reflected in the agency audit. The success of my work was measured by the number of contacts and contact attempts not by the quality of the contacts.

Furthermore, chronological records containing all of my contacts, contact attempts, and case notes, along with any other important information about my offenders, were considered government property. Many times my records were subpoenaed and entered into evidence as "Exhibit A." Therefore, accuracy and honesty were critical. Yes, I needed to document the contact attempt to cover my ass.

These motivating factors combined to necessitate Jake's and my monthly attempt to locate Kyle Beavers. We were sure the last known address was vacant and would be vacant again today. There wasn't even electricity to the house. We always verified residential services with utility companies to determine if one of our absconders was listed as the bill payer. The electricity to Kyle's last known residence was shut off four years ago.

We wanted to return to the office before dark, so I sped down the dirt road towards Kyle's house. Fifteen miles past Mr. Biles' store we entered the Beavers' property. We then turned onto a twin set of ruts across an open field. The grooves in the red dirt were ancient. I didn't notice any new tire marks. Passing two washed out cattle guards we came over the last hill and drove into the front yard of the old house. There, with a tree supporting the leaning side of the structure, Kyle's last known residence rested.

Three generations must have lived in the house. If the walls could talk, they would tell us the stories of Kyle's childhood, the tales of his ninth grade year, and the scenarios after his DUIs. Since there was no discernable driveway, I parked the car next to the pole that once held the mailbox. Like Biles' store, the weathered gray house and pole had never been painted. To the left and behind the house two sheds struggled against the wind. One had been a chicken house, containing yards of wire, and the other was previously a milking barn of sorts. The buckets for collecting the milk and the stools for milking remained, but the cows had long since disappeared. Clouds were starting to form in the north; they piled on top of the house like giant haystacks reaching for the heavens. The fall's first cold front was arriving.

After grabbing my jacket, I crept towards the house. Since Jake and I were dedicated officers, stopping and looking from the car wasn't enough. We had to try the front door and see if anyone or anything answered. Policy required a knock and a business card or note left on the porch. Jake waited in the car, watching me cross the front steps and move towards the broken door.

I was being careful, not because I was fearful, but because the porch was like a mine field. Boards had a nails sticking out or sections of wood were missing or cracked. June bugs hid underneath the rotted wood, and earth worms struggled to escape the impending cold front. The last time I was here, my left leg went through a plank on the porch. I barely pulled it out before a copperhead snake hiding between two broken boards decided to attack. He didn't like my size ten shoes.

I gave the usual, a loud one ... two ... three rapping. Expecting *and* hearing no answer, I placed a business card in what was left of the screen door. As I turned to exit, I heard a creaking board from inside the house. "It must be the wind," I mumbled. To be sure I turned back toward the door to find a set of cold dark eyes staring at me.

"What you want?" insisted the voice behind those eyes.

I was startled. My first thought was I should always expect the unexpected, and this was certainly unexpected.

"You are on private property." I was still trying to locate my lost vocal cords.

"Sir," I cleared my throat, "I'm looking for Kyle Beavers."

"He ain't here. Who are you?"

By this time Jake knew someone was home. He exited the car and moseyed over to my left shoulder next to the unhinged side of the screen door.

"My name is Jack Toliver, and this is Jake Pratt. We are probation officers."

I could still see only shadows of a face and the dark eyes. The shade from the afternoon and the approaching clouds made it difficult for me to identify the speaker.

"You government?" he asked.

"Yes." Jake also nodded a "yes."

"This is Indian land, and you have no right to be here," he instructed.

I understood this was Indian land, which is different from reservation land, but as government officials we had taken the proper protocol. Once per year, we would request and in most cases receive permission from each of the tribal governments to enter. I relayed this to our new found friend.

"So what you want with Kyle?"

"We would like to speak to him since he is on probation, and no one in our office has ever met him," I replied.

"You got a warrant?"

I thought for a moment. Should I or should I not state what I thought was obvious. Why would we be out here looking for someone we had never met and not have a warrant?

"Yes, we have a warrant," I said.

"Let me see it," he held out his right hand to receive the warrant. Not expecting anyone to be at the house, I had left the warrant in the car. Since there was safety in numbers, I couldn't leave Jake on the front porch with the possibility that the dark-eyed man wasn't alone or was armed. Also, if I was talking to Kyle Beavers, I didn't want him to lock the door or run while I went to get the warrant out of the car. So I engaged in probation officer fast talk.

"I did not catch your name?" I inquired.

"I didn't give it." He flipped open a lighter from his back pocket. The small flame highlighted his dark hair and glistened in his eyes. He didn't light a cigarette; he just kept igniting and extinguishing the flame.

"Trust me, I have a warrant, but right now I just want to know if Kyle Beavers is home. Are you Mr. Beavers?" He created a steady flame.

"I might be," he responded noncommittally.

"Why don't you step out on the porch and let's talk?" I coaxed.

I didn't see what Jake must have seen. Our occupant had made a quick move to grab something in the corner next to the inside of the screen door. Jake forced his knee and foot through the screen door, crumbling what remained of the frame. He was taking no chances in case the man was reaching for a weapon. The stranger jerked away from Jake's foot and the screen door while Jake struggled to reach him. They grabbed each other. Jake pulled the man through the door and onto the porch.

Taking a step back, I placed my hand on my weapon, a .38 caliber revolver. (I rarely carried a weapon unless we were making a planned arrest or hunting for absconders.) As Jake attempted to subdue our friend, his eyes grew as big as saucers when he saw me go for my weapon. Jake later told me he thought I was going to shoot both of them. Jake wrestled the young man to the ground and held his face against the broken porch. Then, to no one's surprise, the wood shattered under the weight of the two wrestlers. Jake and his opponent fell through the rotted wood, smashing two June bugs along the way, and I stumbled to maintain my balance.

"Hey man, I'm Beavers! Now get the hell off of me!" he yelled. I never unleashed my weapon but still had my hand on it.

"Not until you quick struggling," Jake grunted.

In all the commotion, I wasn't aware we had visitors. As the two combatants stood up under some newly developed treaty, I noticed other individuals now peering at us from the windows. In addition, two men were standing at both corners of what remained of the porch. I saw them about the same time

Jake did. I clutched my weapon still in its holster. Beavers and Jake noticed my movement. Jake moved away from Beavers while Beavers shook his open hands at me.

"Hey man, no need for that! My brothers and I believe in peace."

Kyle's brothers also shook their hands trying to get me to stop clutching my gun. Jake gave me the look, and I moved my hand to my hip. I knew Jake and I were doing the same critical analyzing. We were out numbered but were we in danger? Jake stood protectively close to Beavers, and I counted five potential familial problems. However, they appeared more surprised and bewildered than we did. No one spoke. I could hear the seconds tick on my watch. Jake couldn't handle the electrified atmosphere.

"Peace? Then what were you grabbing for and why did you resist?" Jake demanded of Beavers.

"Man, I don't want to go to jail, would you? I was locking the door to keep you guys out."

Jake had his handcuffs positioned for a quick latch around Beavers' left wrist, and I was beginning to wonder why he hadn't already handcuffed him. While keeping as much eye as possible on our other guests, I walked towards Jake and Beavers.

"Kyle Beavers, we are going to take you to the county jail for probation violation," I informed him.

Beavers quickly sidled away from Jake as Jake unsuccessfully reached for Beavers' arm. As if it was synchronized dancing, the brothers stepped towards Jake and me. The remaining boards in the porch complained under the strain. The cold metal of Jake's handcuffs hit Beavers' arm.

"Man, I'll go with you; just don't put those things on me. I can't stand them. I'm claustrophobic."

Beavers backed away like a kitten that no longer wanted to play.

The tallest of the brothers pleaded for Beavers. "Hey man, you don't have to do that."

Another professed, "He's good for his word."

The situation was escalating. Jake should have handcuffed Beavers when he had him on the ground, and we should have already placed him the car. I could have driven to the country store by now. Instead, I stood there trying to read Jake's mind. We needed to agree on whatever decision and actions we were going to take.

Assessing our situation, I reminded myself that Kyle Beavers was an infamous absconder. He was six feet tall, muscular, and he was refusing to be handcuffed. His brothers, as he referred to them, were tall, skinny, long haired, and young. I guessed none of them was over 20 years old. After considering my options and remembering that Jake was a man of action, I knew I had to do something and soon. If I didn't act, Jake would wrestle Beavers to the ground, and I would be left to deal with the brothers.

"OK, Mr. Beavers, let's just all calm down and take a breath. No need for anyone to get excited," I paused and used the palms of my hands to push the air towards the ground. I thought the motion would be calming. After everyone seemed to relax, I asked, "What are all you guys doing out here anyway?"

"We were preparing a sweat lodge out back. We come here to sweat, but we hadn't started."

Having partnered with several Native American churches to provide volunteer services that assist offenders, I was somewhat familiar with the sweat lodge process. However, Kyle felt it was necessary to explain.

"Our sweat lodge is here because we use the same rocks and materials our elders have used for generations," he said. "The rocks are better to purify our souls."

The conversation relaxed all of us but Jake. He remained poised for quick action; it must have been his karate training.

"Mr. Beavers, you are in no position to negotiate. We have to handcuff you." Jake grabbed Kyle's arm.

Kyle shook his head in disbelief. "Why do you have to do anything? I'm not armed, and I won't resist. I've already given you my word. My word is good."

"We have policies, and we just might be concerned about our safety," I replied.

Beavers looked at me in a confusing manner. "You're saying my word isn't good with you?"

The sun slid behind the rising clouds, and the brothers started to surround Jake and me. They were listening intently to this direct but philosophical dialogue.

"No, I'm not saying your word is no good. I'm just saying that for all of us – including you – it is safer if you are handcuffed. Besides it's a policy."

"Who wrote this policy?" Beavers asked.

Out of frustration, I answered, "I don't know. It is just a policy we have to follow. Stop trying to change the subject."

"That is your policy and not mine, so I don't have to follow it. You have followed policy by requesting that I submit to handcuffing, and I have respectfully declined. Since it isn't my policy, we are in compliance."

Beavers should have been on my high school debating team. Before I could formulate an intelligent response, Beavers stepped backwards and the brothers stepped forward. They then interlocked their arms together. For a moment, I thought we had been beamed back to the early 1970s. Was this act of resistance a peaceful protest? This was getting difficult.

Should I have:
A.   Left and never said a word about this to anyone.
B.   Grabbed and started untwisting arms.
C.   Ordered Jake to stay while I went for back up.
D.   Given in to Beavers and transported him without handcuffs.
E.   Invited Jake and myself to the sweat lodge purification.
F.   Let Jake practice his karate.

"You guys are going to make this difficult," Jake remarked as he stepped toward the pretzel mass.

"Now Jake, let's wait a minute," I suggested. "Mr. Beavers, you agree to go with us and not cause any trouble?"

"Yes, my brothers and I'll go."

I assumed his continued referral to the others as brothers wasn't a reference to biological relatives. Nonetheless, I had to ask. "Are they really your brothers?"

"They are my brothers like you are my brother but more so since you don't appear to be from my tribe."

I knew he was trying to be funny, but I didn't laugh.

"Here's the deal. My partner here will ride in the back with you, and you won't have to be handcuffed."

Kyle and the brothers agreed, and we all walked towards the Citation. Jake opened the door and Beavers slid into the back seat accompanied by his five tribal brothers.

"Wait a minute," I demanded. "All of you guys can't go. Get out of the car." No one followed my demand. As a matter of fact, they continued to rearrange themselves in an effort to become more comfortable.

"Get out of the car," I yelled. Again, they continued to adjust positions so that eight of us could fit into the car.

"If my brothers don't go, I don't go," Beavers argued.

I looked at Jake and he just shrugged his shoulders and gave me a look; the same look he exhibited when I told Mommy Dearest that she misunderstood what I had said; a look that communicates, "You started this. Now you finish it."

There was something calming and trusting about Kyle Beavers. I don't know if it was his manners, speech, or commitment, but I believed him.

"Why do they have to go?" I asked, searching for any viable reason that five men would want to venture to the county jail.

Beavers looked at me as if I should already know the answer to this rudimentary question. "They have warrants too."

"What?" Jake asked.

"Well, I'm sure they do," Beavers answered. "We've been in hiding for awhile. I assumed they were hiding from the law."

"That doesn't explain anything," I followed up.

"You see, let's just say I came into a considerable amount of money from my family. Me and my brothers decided you only live once, and since wealth never really was a concern of ours, we decided to rid ourselves of it all. So we've been traveling, and, well, we left the county with some unfinished business. Edger here has a bogus check charge or two pending that I think he missed a court date on."

Edger smiled like he had just been introduced to an applauding crowd of thousands.

"Tommy and Allen have been wanted on questioning for hunting elk out of season. Oh yes, they also had some little problem with an assault situation. Karl and Larry, you never know who wants them for what," Beavers explained.

"Plus we don't have a car. I gave it away today. You can't leave them out here without electricity."

"So all you guys are wanted for something?" I asked, ignoring the car and electricity comments.

"That's a possibility," Edger said impassively.

I took a deep breath and exhaled with caution. "What to do, what to do," I said in a whisper guaranteed to be inaudible. My usual stubbornness and tenacity had been weakened by the day's events.

"What the hell," I said. "Everybody, let's go." With a mumble Jake confirmed my decision.

"First everybody out, we can't go anywhere until I'm convinced no one is carrying anything dangerous."

They all understood and piled out of the back seat. Pulling pockets wrong side out and patting down pant legs, they assisted Jake and me in a thorough search. When we didn't find any weapons, our six passengers, leg on leg, hip on hip squeezed into the car so that Jake could shut the doors. Jake couldn't fit into the backseat, and the brothers weren't interested in sitting in the front seat. Jake settled in as the passenger and secured his seat belt, all the while twisting his body around to face our voluntary captives.

With all the additional weight in the rear of our Citation, traveling the dirt road back to the main highway was treacherous. When the ruts in the field deepened, we encountered a mishap. The high center of the car drug along the dried mud and grass, and our muffler became a distant image in the rear view mirror. We proceeded, making loud small talk over the roar of a muffler-less car. When I couldn't think of any more minor questions to ask Mr. Beavers, I had to know, "How much money did you have?"

"Around a million and a half or so, I don't exactly remember," Beavers answered.

"What the hell did you do with it all?"

"This and that: I bought a few cars, took a few trips, bought several houses for my mother and other family, partied a lot, and just stuff like that."

By the time we arrived at the county jail, everyone was describing how the money was spent. "We had a great time in Vegas," Edgar gleefully interjected.

"Yeah, and the Camaro we bought was great," said Larry.

I had to silence the chit chat when we reached the deserted parking lot of the county jail. Reaching the vehicle entrance, I stretched to reach the intercom and spoke into the speaker mounted next to the entry gate of the sally port.

"This is probation officers Pruitt and Toliver. We have Kyle Beavers on a county probation warrant and several others who may be wanted." I waited for a response.

"You have what?" the distant voice in the speaker asked.

"I said we have Kyle Beavers and several others who may be wanted."

"How many others?"

"Oh, maybe five," I said in a matter of fact tone.

Squeaking and rattling, the gate slowly opened. An elderly jailer greeted our Citation with a shotgun and a grim expression. Jake opened the back door to pry our captives out. Upon seeing they weren't handcuffed, our jailer became nervous, backed up, and leveled his shot gun.

Jake raised his hands and said, "Hold on there. No need for any alarm. These guys are all volunteers."

"What did you do? Hypnotize them into submission?" the jailer asked incredulously.

We proceeded into the holding area of the jail and awaited processing. Beavers was correct. All of the men were wanted for something; however, Edgar had the only felony pending. Before the county jailer took Kyle and the brothers to their cells, they shook Jake's and my hands and thanked us for not leaving them in the country without electricity. Beavers also thanked us for accepting his word and maintaining his dignity. He assured me if given another chance, he would report as required. Then he added a caveat. He would only report if I was his officer.

Before we left the jail, the officer in charge of Kyle and the brothers commented about the enormous pile of paper work we had given him. He was obviously in awe of our absconder hunting ability and our courage in capturing these desperados. When asked how we did it, Jake simply said, "We surrounded them."

In the end, maybe we violated policy and maybe we did the right thing for the right reason, but Jake and I both knew, even though we didn't verbally acknowledge it, we were damn lucky. We deserved an onion burger, fries, and watered down coke.

Chapter Six
"Until Death Do Us Part"

"Perpetual Halloween," I kept thinking. "This whole apartment reso-
nates Halloween."

One by one I felt the hairs on my leg part. Maybe the morning chill
fighting against the overheated apartment caused the sensation, but I doubted
it. There it was again. Something wasn't crawling but skipping or hopping
across my ankle and up my leg. A quick slap to the lower thigh, and it disappeared. Still waiting for her to return from her phone call, I scratched my ankle
with the heel of my shoe, anticipating the sensation's return.

The orange and black shag carpet consisted of many natural parts, much
like those found on my Tibetan terrier. Faded in spots and stained and matted
in others, the carpet died two decades ago. A Roman pillar lamp dimly illumi-
nated the apartment, and the window drapes, black and orange of course, battled
with the advancing rays of sunshine.

Outside of the apartment, the leaves were changing colors and a cool breeze
passed over the ground, but somehow the apartment rejected the fall morning.
Opening one of the drapes briefly crossed my mind, but I was convinced their
frailty couldn't withstand the pressure. Furthermore, if the light invaded the
space, I feared the room would disintegrate like a vampire.

I watched her walk across the hallway into the bathroom, still talking on
the phone. When I arrived earlier, she answered the door, acted as if she knew
who I was, didn't asked for identification, and told me to sit down. She went to
put on a robe and then answered the telephone, leaving me in the living room
of her apartment with a burnt orange velvet sofa staring at me from across the
room.

Composed of three equal sections, the sofa formed an "L" shape, directing traffic towards the kitchen. I sat on the sister to the sofa: a pumpkin colored chair with a rather large derriere indention in the cushion. Repeatedly sinking deeply into the chair, I had to place my hands on my lap because my limbs wouldn't comfortably reach the arm rests.

To the back and sides of the television and its antenna covered in tin foil was a thick layer of aged dust. In addition, the dust provided a protective blanket over the chair, the sofa, and, come to mention it, everything in the apartment. In the corner, stacked on the combination turntable and eight-track stereo, was a collection of Barry White's and Al Green's greatest hits: vinyls, not eight-tracks. I saw only one eight-track tape, Queen's "We Are the Champions."

Watching her return to the bedroom, I damned the sensation from my leg once again and tried to understand my surroundings. Her apartment was in a complex called New Hope Village, which was the city's attempt to provide clean and adequate subsidized housing. I questioned the "clean" aspect of the endeavor and renamed the complex "No Hope Village."

Most people, including me, believed it was an attempt to put parolees and anyone with the potential to be on some type of caseload all in one location. I benefited from the arrangement because I could make numerous field contacts in a short amount of time. Furthermore, the residents knew all the probation officers. Sometimes, New Hope Village looked like a state employee convention. Human Services, Mental Health, and other state agencies had employees working with apartment residents on a daily basis.

On numerous occasions, I had tried to schedule an appointment with Ms. Dorothy Johnson, but she avoided the meeting. As a last resort, I arrived unannounced. Ms. Johnson was my third pre-sentence investigation in the last month. I was still thinking about the other two interviews when she returned, rubbing her eyes and scratching her behind.

She offered me a cup of coffee, but I declined. Even if policy allowed me to accept refreshments from clients, I would never take a drink from her in this environment. She told me she was thirsty and followed the "L" sofa towards the refrigerator. Since the apartment hid little from my view, I watched as she used her long fingernails to scrape the mold from inside her jack-o-lantern coffee cup. She smiled as if suspecting the hot coffee she was pouring wouldn't only taste good and aid in her awakening, but would also disinfect the mug.

Her hand inadvertently brushed aside two elderly cockroaches perched on the side of the cabinet. Unlike most cockroaches, these two moved methodically and slowly ... almost confidently. Maybe they were fat and lazy, or maybe they knew their beloved Dorothy wasn't an imminent threat. Just maybe, they were pets. Dorothy, even slower than the cockroaches, moved around the kitchen and worked her way back to the interview. Entertaining myself, waiting her return, I named the cockroaches Roter and Rooter.

Ms. Johnson sat on the sofa and stretched her legs to correspond with the L shape. She took a quick sip of coffee and lit a partial cigarette she had discovered in the over turned ash tray on the floor. She appeared to be the most carefree, content person I had ever met.

Beginning with the basics for a pre-sentence investigation report: profile information, relatives, education, and employment along with financial background and criminal history, I didn't hear any surprises. She dropped out of school in the tenth grade, had only minimum wage jobs, hadn't worked in three years, divorced once, widowed twice, and loved the color orange.

Her criminal history included a deferred sentence for shoplifting resulting in diversion, two dismissed misdemeanor assault charges, a citation for failure to appear, numerous bogus check charges with unconfirmed dispositions, and welfare fraud. In addition, she had given birth to three children. The son was in prison for manslaughter in the second degree, and one daughter lived somewhere in the New Hope Village complex. The youngest and third child resided on the East Coast, but Dorothy didn't know where. She claimed this child had received a full scholarship to Dartmouth and after graduation she had never returned.

I continued the interview with questions related to the current offense. She was charged with forgery and bank fraud and took satisfaction in her creative criminal process. She told me intricate details about her camera with a 500 meter zoom lens and a speed winder to take photos of people utilizing ATMs. When one of her victims approached an ATM, Dorothy would snap a photo of their card as they placed it in the machine, then snap photos as they pressed their PIN numbers. After developing the photos, she used their identification to order items over the phone or through the internet, depending on which method was easier for Dorothy.

I asked if she had a computer and she told me it was taken as evidence and probably wouldn't be returned. I requested a written statement concerning her version of the offense, but she simply referred to the district attorney's official version, claiming the statement was extremely accurate and right on the money. Concluding the interview with an assessment for assistance and formalized supervision plan for the recommendation and summary section of the pre-sentence investigation, I started gathering my materials to leave and asked one last question.

"Ms. Johnson, do you have any remorse for your action?"

She pulled the finished cigarette out of her mouth and placed it gently on the floor. As she thought, the parting hairs on my leg interrupted my observations. I couldn't take it any longer. Bending down, I clawed at my ankles. She didn't notice my anguish and wrinkled her nose in thought.

Still scratching, I recalled a weekend expedition in the park that Alvin, my two year old pit bull, and I took. Did I catch some form of poison ivy or get chiggers?

She finally answered, rubbing her tongue against her coffee and nicotine stained teeth. "Mr. Anderson, I haven't given that question much thought, but in honesty, I would say no. No one was injured, and I would guess insurance covered their losses."

"Do you feel obligated to pay restitution?"

Intrigued by the question, she stirred her coffee with her fingernail, careful not to let the liquid touch her finger tip. She looked at me, flared her nostrils, and said, "Don't think so."

Even though I couldn't wait to leave the apartment, I didn't let the conversation end. "Have you ever had a substance abuse problem?" I asked.

She crossed and then uncrossed her ankles, embedded her left hand into her hair, twisted her fingers, frowned, and looked toward Roter and Rooter still sitting on the kitchen cabinet.

"You'd have to define substance," she said.

I was now scratching my knees, and her request caught me somewhat off balance.

"You know alcohol, legal and illegal drugs," I answered.

"Well in that case, the answer is no," she said.

Curiosity overtook me, creating an impulse to ask a quick follow-up question. "What substances were you thinking of?"

"There's the obvious: nicotine, caffeine, pure oxygen, and there is the not so obvious." She seemed uncomfortable; I changed tactics.

"Do you want to continue this line of questioning?"

"Not really," she said.

I enquired about her two deceased husbands. She nonchalantly replied, "Oh they just had heart attacks."

Since Ms. Johnson was only thirty-six years old, I had to ask the obvious. "Were they older than you?"

"Yes, as a matter of fact they were. Both were about a year older."

Using logic, since her last husband died three years ago, he would have had a heart attack in his early thirties, somewhat unusual. I noted the math and continued discussing the deceased's general health. I learned both husbands were overweight, smoked, did drugs, and lead a sedentary life. The conversation morphed into the benign.

I contemplated many more probing questions, but by now my ankles and lower legs required constant scratching. I concluded my visit, thanked her for her time, and informed her I would verify her work history, prior residences, and other information. I also mentioned that she would have to come to my office for a required second visit. She commented that she didn't like to leave the house and would prefer that I come to see her. I left all options open since she had been so difficult to contact this time and since I wanted to leave the apartment as soon as possible. Shaking my hand, I could feel her fake nails on my fingers; she thanked me for coming and asked if I would be her probation officer. "I don't know, and I'm not sure if you will receive probation," I responded.

"Oh, I'll get probation," Ms Johnson advised. "I already have an arrangement with the district attorney. I provided him with information about the drug dealers in the apartment complex and who shot Willy Loomis."

I shook my head in disbelief.

"Ms. Johnson, this is too much information." I had to leave. I moved towards the front door; the morning air beckoned. "What I mean is, you shouldn't be telling anyone this if it is true. What you do with the prosecutor's office will have no bearing on my recommendation to the court in this presentence report or on your supervision if you do, in fact, receive a probated sentence."

"Just thought I'd let you know. It's always good to know things. Information like this may come in handy some day," she said, turning her back and walking towards the sofa.

Finally, I turned to exit the apartment. As the door closed, I heard a hissing sound and saw Ms. Johnson spraying the carpet with some sort of pesticide. I closed the door behind me and stepped out into the stark contrast of the morning. Brilliant sunlight quickly cleansed me of the mustiness in my nostrils and the rainbow of odors I transported from her apartment to the disinfecting outdoors.

Once in the sun, I raised the legs of my pants and noticed what appeared to be two quarter inch black tattoos encircling my ankles. As the heat hit the tattoos, they slithered like a snake, spiraling downward into my socks. Dropping to one knee, I grabbed my left sock with one hand and with the other I captured half of the moving tattoo. When I opened my hand to investigate, I found a plethora of jumping and jiving fleas.

I had fleas! I sat on the ground just a few feet outside Ms. Johnson's door and quickly rid myself of socks and shoes. Then I realized this course of action wouldn't be enough. In my haste, I discovered that the fleas didn't appreciate the sun. Therefore the little bastards were running up my leg, and even worse they were also scrambling up my pants. Gathering my shoes and socks, skipping with the pace of a sprinter across the graveled parking lot to my car, I spun my tires and kicked-up dust and gravel like I had just committed a bank robbery.

I learned a valuable lesson that day: fleas do not die easily. I also learned that they breed and multiply more prodigiously than rabbits and, along with cockroaches, they will be the only living creatures on earth after Armageddon. In addition, I painfully learned that they thrived in the carpet of my car and my house, laid eggs, had babies, and cost me almost $1,500 for the Orkin man, not to mention medication for my thousands of bites.

I filed my pre-sentence report on Ms. Johnson without having to re-enter her Halloween zone. Since she had been candidly honest, I easily verified her information: employment, relatives, financial history, etc. And she was correct; she received a two year deferred sentence and was placed on probation. I wasn't an attorney, so I had no business telling the court she wasn't eligible for such a sentence. Besides, I thought they knew. If she was willing to give me information and openly discuss her criminal practices, surely she also told her attorney.

Since luck always seemed to elude me, I wasn't surprised when I had to supervise Dorothy Johnson's case. Until her judgment and sentence appeared in my box, I had forgotten about Dorothy, Roter and Roder, and the Orkin man. I opened the case without another intake interview; however, I still needed to contact Dorothy.

To avoid visiting her at home, I sent several delinquent notices to her residence. I couldn't call her apartment because the phone had been disconnected two months before. She never contacted me. Considering my options, I was either going to have to declare her an absconder or spoon feed her through probation for two years. I decided to start with spoon feeding and a reality lecture even if I had to make a home visit to get my point across.

Preparing myself for a visit with the infamous, I placed rubber bands around my ankles and at the top of my socks. This, hopefully, would keep the little devils from entering and hiding. I also sprayed my pants, my shoes, and my socks with the most expensive pesticide known to man. I took an extra can of the industrial strength spray to leave in my car in case another attack occurred.

In the five months since I had visited No Hope Village, the paint had already begun to peel and the speed bumps in the driveway had disappeared. Parking as close as possible to Dorothy's apartment, I still had to walk across one yard, down two small sidewalks between several units, and follow a yellow brick road. I hummed tunes from *The Wizard of Oz* while passing the emerald colored apartments. Reaching Dorothy's home and taking a deep breath, I knocked on the door. The drapes rustled inside, but no one answered.

"Dorothy, I know you are in there. This is your probation officer, so open up."

More noise was coming from inside. I even heard a little giggle. If I was going to hide from my probation officer, I would be as quiet as possible. I almost banged on the door before it cracked open a few inches.

"My name is Ashley. What's yours?"

I looked down and saw a little munchkin with big brown eyes looking up at me. This girl, about four years old, had her hair pulled back into a tight set of pig tails with orange strings covering the rubber bands. She wore a miniature set of Tommy Boy designer jeans and a red sweater. She also apparently had a bad encounter with a chocolate candy bar. Much of it was smeared on her face and outlined her lips; however, her hands were surprisingly clean. I told her my name and asked where her parents were.

"I live with Dorothy," she said.

"Is Dorothy a relative?" I asked.

"What's a relative?" Ashley replied.

I didn't have time to answer before the door opened wide. A rather tall woman with freshly painted fingernails and tightly curled hair stood in the doorway. She smelled like Chenille and cigarettes.

"Afternoon Ma'am, have you seen Dorothy Johnson?" She smiled, giggled, twisted her hair, and pulled at her curls.

"You don't remember me?"

Little Ashley grabbed the woman's leg and said, "This is my momma."

A closer look revealed Dorothy's coffee and nicotine stained teeth and casual attitude.

"This is my new husband's child," Dorothy explained.

I stared at a transformed Ms. Johnson. Her hair was recently fashioned.

She wore makeup and had on what appeared to be an expensive dress and pair of high heels accented by customized fingernails. It was quite different than bath-robed woman I met previously.

She invited me in, and Ashley promised to show me her new doll. When I entered the apartment, there wasn't the sharp contrast between the outdoors and the living room as before. The now open drapes had been replaced with new Venetian blinds, and tile appeared where the flea-infested carpet used to be. In addition, a huge flat screen television hung on the wall. My favorite cockroaches were no where in sight. The transformation distracted me, but I regained my composure. Sitting in a new leather chair, I prepared for battle. Just because everything was new, didn't mean the army of fleas had been defeated.

"You have a new husband?" I inquired.

"Yes, I was married the day after I received probation."

Ashley took a liking to me and squeezed in beside me in the oversized leather chair, holding her doll by its leg.

"My dad's asleep in the bedroom. Do you want me to go get him?" Ashley asked. She twisted her mouth and batted her eyes wanting me to reply.

"Ashley, go outside and play," demanded Dorothy. Ashley hung her head and scooted toward the door. She looked back at me expecting a reprieve. I didn't ask her to stay, so she studied the floor for a moment and then took her doll outside.

I had questions for the transformed Ms. Johnson, but first things first. I admonished Dorothy for not reporting.

"This isn't a game." I told her. While I explained the consequences of such continued behavior, she appeared unfazed. I didn't expect any revelations, but I at least thought she would listen. She filled out a monthly report and promised to pay probation fees and restitution in full by next week. With the basics covered, curiosity got the better of me.

"Ms. Johnson, you certainly have done some remodeling. Did your new husband do all of this?" I tried to sound friendly rather than nosey.

"He did most of the work. I finally got my insurance settlement from my last husband, so I could afford to clean this place up a little bit."

"Who's your new husband?"

"I thought you knew. He reports to your office. I think the name of his officer his Wayne."

"He's on probation?" I pretended to be shocked, but I wasn't really surprised.

"No, he's on parole out of Texas. Shot a cop down there about fifteen years ago." I mentally searched for any parolee that would fit the profile, but I couldn't identify her husband.

"What's his name?" I had to know.

"Willie Farmer."

A toilet flushed in the background. Turning off the bathroom light, a tall, skinny, shirtless man, doing his best to hold up his baggy pajama bottoms, entered the room. He had bullet entry scars on his chest and a large incision running the length of his abdomen. He came over, shook my hand, and lit a cigarette.

"Were you talking about me?" Willie asked. "Hey man," he waved his cigarette at me. "You think one of us could report for both of us?" I waved the smoke out of my face.

"We might be able to arrange for one officer to supervise both of you, but everybody will have to report," I replied.

Since this was all that interested him, he kissed Dorothy and went back into the bedroom. Smiling, she showed me the door and bid me farewell, promising to report the next time I summoned her.

Back at the office, I spoke to Wayne, who graciously agreed to allow Willie to be on my caseload. Once again, it was a matter of workload units. My caseload was smaller than his, and he was all too willing to give me the responsibility.

Reviewing Willie Farmer's file, I found out that he was a Texas bad boy. Most of his life had been spent either in prison or under some type of community supervision. Like Dorothy, he also knew the criminal justice system well. He had shot a police officer in Dallas when a drug task force raided his home. He claimed self defense citing that he thought the cop was a burglar. The courts gave him a split sentence. There must have been something wrong with the arrest because five years in prison and five years on parole for shooting a police officer seemed lenient.

I don't know why I expected anything different, but another month went by with no sign from Dorothy or Willie. If the Texas Interstate Compact office hadn't requested a progress and conduct report on Willie, I wouldn't have ventured back to their apartment. I would have sent a delinquent notice to both of them and waited them out. Because of Willie's assessed risk level, a home visit was due next month anyway. Dorothy was assessed at a lower risk level and home visits weren't required. Cutting my losses, I decided to go to No Hope Village.

Ashley opened the door after the first knock. When she curtseyed, I could smell the old familiar musty odor. "My step momma ain't here, but my dad is."

I leaned down to talk to her. "Ashley, please tell your dad to come to the door."

"OK," she said, turning and running toward the bedroom. I stayed in the doorway, watching for Willie. She returned carrying the doll she had on my last visit.

"My daddy won't wake up," she said.

I convinced her to try again. This time, when she returned, she came back to the door without the doll.

"He must be really sleepy. He won't wake up."

In this strange situation, should I have:

A. Told Ashley to throw some water on him.
B. Gone inside to wake him up myself.
C. Counted it as a home visit and move on.
D. Yelled fire and gone inside to wake him up.

Ashley made the decision for me when she looked up at me with angelic innocence, "Would you help me wake my daddy up?"

She reached out and took my hand in hers and led me through the house. I guess I could have said "no" but going with her seemed like the right thing to do at the time. We entered the bedroom where I saw Willie wrapped in blankets from head to toe. The covering gave him a mummified appearance even though I couldn't see any of his body, only the outline.

Ashley walked to the bed and cautiously shook her daddy. "Please, Daddy, please wake up. Mr. Probation Officer is here."

Willie didn't move. I walked slowly to the bed with my hand extended. If this was a set up, I was going to be prepared.

"Sorry to have to wake you Mr. Farmer," I said, "but I really need to speak to you."

There was no movement or sound. I momentarily studied the patterns on the patch work quilt covering his body and watched for any sign of movement. Hearing and seeing nothing coming from the bed, I reached over and shook Willie by the leg. The wood like texture and stiffness of his body startled me. However, I showed no surprise and tried to not upset Ashley.

"Ashley, could you give me a glass of water?" I asked.

When Ashley left the room, I pulled the covers back just far enough to see

Willie's face. His clouded eyes were open, and he had dried matter across his cheek. I touched his face with the back of my hand and felt the cold lifelessness of his skin. I placed the quilt over his corpse before Ashley returned with a toy tea cup of water.

"Ashley, let's go outside and let your dad rest," I said. I took her hand this time, and we walked into the sunshine.

"Do you have a neighbor you can visit for a moment while I make a phone call?" Ashley told me her stepmother's daughter lived in the apartment complex. I had forgotten about Dorothy's daughter.

Ashley and I walked over to another stand of apartments to what I guessed was her half sister's home. Banging on the door, I was surprised when Dorothy and her daughter answered. Ashley ran in to play with a child that appeared to be close to her age. I asked Ms. Johnson to step into the hallway.

"Ms. Johnson, I've been to your apartment. Ashley invited me in to help wake up her father. I'm afraid I have some bad news for you." I paused for a moment, expecting Dorothy to ask about the news, but she waited for me to continue.

"Willie is dead."

Dorothy didn't change expressions.

"Are you sure?" she asked.

"Yes I'm sure."

"He had been complaining of chest pains and an upset stomach. I told him to quit being so lazy and go to the doctor."

"Dorothy," I said, "one of us needs to call the police."

"Would you do it?" she asked.

"Sure, I'll do it."

I stepped inside and used the phone. I called the police who in turn called an ambulance. Waiting outside for the authorities, I wanted to question Dorothy, but the timing was inappropriate.

"Do you think I might get off probation early?" Dorothy asked. "Now that Willie is dead, I think I'll go back east."

Willie hadn't even been removed from the apartment, and Dorothy was already making plans to move on.

The police and the ambulance arrived to take care of the body. As they were closing the ambulance doors the medic turned to me, "Man that guy could've been ripe. Bet he's been dead for at least two days. Lucky for a good, cold air conditioner, hey?"

I nodded as if I understood. Instead of following her husband, Dorothy disappeared into the house. I followed to inquire if there was anything I could do for her. Crossing the kitchen and down the hall, I found her going through Willie's pants and extracting a billfold.

"Ms. Johnson, is there anything I can do for you?"

"No thank you." She replied.

I figured now wasn't the time to admonish Dorothy for her poor probationer behavior, so I gave her another business card and asked her to call when she felt better. I wasn't sure why I said that because she appeared to be feeling just fine.

Two weeks went by and I hadn't heard from Dorothy. Nevertheless, I did read Willie Farmer's obituary.

"Willie Farmer, beloved father and faithful husband, died of a heart attack last Thursday."

Another week passed before I decided to contact Dorothy. This time I was going to put my "no nonsense" face on, and in no uncertain terms, demand full compliance with reporting requirements. As I walked up to her door, a man, part of the apartment maintenance staff, yelled at me from across the parking lot.

"She moved," he yelled.

"Did she say where she was moving?" I cupped my hands around my mouth in order to yell back.

"They never tell," he said.

I couldn't remember the apartment number of her daughter but by luck and a good sense of direction, I located it. Again, Ashley greeted me at the door and introduced me to her step sister, Salinas. They were either watching for me or heard my conversation with the maintenance man. In a soft and kind voice, Salinas invited me in. Ashley quickly found a spot beside me and started talking faster than I could understand. She mumbled something about day care, new friends, and an evil teacher.

"My mother moved to Boston last week," Salinas offered, unsolicited. "She said you would probably come by, so she asked me to give these to you."

Salinas handed me two large legal sized envelopes. One contained a cashier's check for full payment of restitution and a money order for two years worth of probation fee payments. The other contained a court order from her sentencing judge making the remainder of her probation sentence unsupervised. To say the least, I was astonished. I asked several questions related to the payment and court orders, but Salinas had no answers. She did inform me that Willie's mother was still alive but couldn't take care of Ashley.

"I'm trying to qualify to be her foster parent. The state'll pay me to keep her until a decision is made. Don't worry. The case worker has already approved her to stay here and is supposed to come by the house twice a week."

Ashley dropped her doll. Salinas picked it up, straightening Ashley's pig tails in the process.

After leaving No Hope Village, I drove to the court house and secured certified copies of the release from supervision and an order allowing Dorothy to leave the state, which I also found in the court clerk's file.

There were benefits to having close professional relationships with local prosecutors and judges. Depending upon an officer's longevity and the size of the local judicial district, such relationships could enhance and systematize operations and communications, which proved beneficial in this case. While at the court house I leisurely paid a visit to Dorothy's prosecutor. She was in her rectangular office designed to accommodate every law book ever published.

Standing at one end of her conference table, which was affixed to her desk in a "T" formation, I felt as if I was perched at the end of a bar room shuffleboard. Leaning with both elbows on the table I cleared my throat to draw her attention to me.

"Officer Anderson, what gives me the pleasure of your visit?" Ms. Barsel asked, casually looking up at me and pushing her glasses back to the arch of her nose. After asking her usual ice breaker, she returned to reading the law book in front of her. As with the hundreds of conversations we had had before, I knew she was still paying attention to me.

"I was wondering what was up with Dorothy Johnson? I understand you petitioned the court and had her removed her from supervised probation."

"It just seemed like the thing to do. I saw no harm in it because if she gets arrested we can still revoke her until the original expiration date."

I quickly surmised she didn't expect me to like this cozy answer. "I don't recall you ever doing this before," I said.

"Oh, I may not have. I can't remember every little thing I've done since I took this job."

She peered at me over her glasses and rolled her eyes. "Look, I know you can read between the lines. You've been around a long time. I appreciate the fact I don't have to spell it out for you so quit having fun at my expense. Now, how's that ex-Hell's Angel I took a chance on by agreeing to a suspended sentence for Conspiracy to Commit a Felony? You know, I figured he was old enough to fall into that research I read last month. The research said something to the affect that offenders over fifty have low recidivism rates and are less likely to fail probation."

"He's doing fine and should be no problem. And you didn't get me off the subject. Did you know this was Dorothy Johnson's third dead husband, and they all died of heart attacks?"

She looked shocked that I had more information than she did. For once, the probation and parole officer had bested the attorney.

"No, I didn't know that, but it sounds like she either has a lot of bad luck or marries guys on their deathbeds," she said. "You know, bad diets and drugs will kill you eventually."

"Cute, but didn't it occur to you that maybe, just maybe Dorothy has a system?"

Closing her book, she leaned back in her chair, finally giving the matter the attention I craved. "What are you getting at?" she asked.

"Well, I think Dorothy has made a good living off of her marriages in that, when her husbands die, insurance pay-outs become her income. When the income gets low, she finds another husband."

I told her about the tin foil antenna on the television from my first visit and the flat screen TV hanging on the wall on my second visit. Also, the new furniture and how the fleas and carpet were replaced with tiles.

"So, you're saying she shops for husbands who are in poor health and then waits until they die?

"No, what I'm saying is, what if she finds low-life individuals who she is sure no one, especially the police, care if they live or die, and then kills them? Willie Farmer came out of nowhere and was a police shooter. He had very little family. I wonder if he fit the other husbands' profiles."

Ms. Barsel's went back to looking at her book; I had lost her attention. "You need a vacation, Officer Max Anderson. Don't you think that's a little far fetched?"

"It's just a theory. When I told her Willie was dead, she showed no emotion and asked if I thought she could get off of probation early. Also, even though I thought nothing of it at the time, she was evasive about her family history and prior marriages during the intake interview. I just have some weird feelings about this ... professionally and otherwise."

"What's the otherwise feeling?"

"I guess just plain old male intuition," I responded.

"Max, I'll tell you what I'll do. When I get a chance, I'll have my investigator make a few calls, check out your silly male intuition, and we'll see where it goes. Send over your file on her, and we'll check out what I prefer to call a hunch."

"Ms. Barsel, what's in a word? Male intuition or a hunch, I still believe this will go somewhere."

She licked her fingers, flipping the pages in her book. I knew the discussion was over.

I had almost forgotten about my visit with District Attorney Barsel until her investigator Chris Boren called three weeks later. Chris informed me that Dorothy, not her husbands, purchased life insurance policies. He also claimed that Dorothy had to pay high premiums because her husbands were poor insurance risks, and she even had to pay for medical physicals to qualify them for insurance.

Of her two previous husbands, one was buried in Louisiana and the other was buried in Texas but died in Tennessee. Willie Farmer was buried in the cemetery down the road. According to the records at the funeral home, a local church paid for his burial. The funeral director reported Dorothy didn't attend the simple graveside service because her daughter was ill. Dorothy had to leave the state to take care of her child. Since her husband just died, her daughter was sick, and Dorothy claimed to have no money, the funeral director contacted a church, who paid for Dorothy's trip east.

Chris finished his personal observations stating all the dead husbands had been menaces to society with lengthy felony records, and if Dorothy had somehow killed them, she should get a medal. The conversation took an unsuspected turn when I found out Ms. Barsel had requested, and Judge Adams had approved, exhuming Willie's body because the other husbands hadn't had an autopsy. The medical examiner would perform the autopsy within the next seven days.

Almost a week to the day, I stopped by my favorite Starbucks, and while standing in line for a vanilla latte, I read the headlines:

"Coroner Rules Local Death a Homicide"

I grabbed the paper and read the article.

"What was originally ruled a death by natural causes, heart attack, has now been reversed. District Attorney Barsel said a charge of Murder in the First Degree will be filed this week for Ms. Dorothy Johnson. Barsel states there was enough common rat poisoning in Farmer's blood to kill three men. She also confirmed two other states would be investigating Johnson and the deaths of her two previous husbands. When asked what led to exhuming the body and the subsequent autopsy, Barsel simply stated, 'Good probation work.'"

I sipped my latte and sat down to finish the article. However, before I could, I received a message on my pager, "Barbara from the Daily Record News wants to interview you about Dorothy Johnson." I guess Ms. Barsel gave me some credit.

It has been two years since charges were filed against Dorothy. Even though there is a warrant for her arrest, her whereabouts are still unknown.

Chapter Seven
"Alfalfa"

My district supervisor, Gil Kleen, never paid much attention to congenial protocol. He believed in straightforwardness, making his conversations short and his reprimands painful. For example, when a politician would ask him why I or another officer was either too tough or too lenient with a client, he would call us directly.

"Mark," he would threaten, "the only thing constant in life is change. Now what the hell do I need to change around here?"

Apart from his attitude, he had survived the administrative alterations of the last twenty years, and he had gained my respect. When he called, I always listened.

On the morning of the twenty-third, the week of harvest, my officemate, Claude Mendoza, went to the courthouse, leaving me to clean the office. It was our weekly ritual. Every Wednesday, one or both of us would wash the stained coffee cups and clear the paper work off the desk. Since we shared a small confined space, we had to maintain some sense of order. As I tried to peel the mold out of my Father's Day mug, the red light lit up on my telephone. I knew immediately who wanted to speak to me. If Mr. Kleen called, the receptionist would use the third phone line, the line connected to the red light.

"Good morning Mr. Kleen. What can I do for you?"

"Well, good morning to you too, Officer Casey. I'm at the division office today, and we need a little help. I thought since you are a veteran officer that you could lend me a hand."

I put down the coffee mug and leaned back in my chair. Mr. Kleen never called for help; he usually called to yell. In addition, he never referred to me as a "veteran" officer. I had worked for the department for twenty-one years, had no plans for retirement, and had never heard such a flattering yet frightening term.

"You know I'm here to serve, just ask and you shall receive," I responded in my usual up beat attitude. He chuckled, an out of the ordinary response.

"Well, don't be so quick to volunteer your services," he paused to tell his receptionist to hold his calls. "You don't know what I need."

Now he had my full attention and curiosity. Mr. Kleen never beat around the bush, and he never made small talk.

"Look, Mr. Casey, this is a little unusual. Well, hell, it is just a damn doosey."

I waited for him to continue as he sucked in a lung full of air and took thirty seconds to exhale. "I guess there is only one way to do this," he confided.

I pandered, "I'm sure I can handle it, and if I can't, I'll be completely discreet."

Now that I had reassured Mr. Kleen he continued.

"Our new governor has chosen to exercise an obscure law on the books. Well, I guess it's not necessarily a law, but, anyway, he used it. He chose to place an inmate who's in a medium security prison on administrative leave."

I needed to clarify, "You mean like a weekend pass?"

"No, not really."

"More like a furlough then," I offered.

"No, more like *administrative leave*," Mr. Kleen was starting to question his decision to call me instead of another officer.

"What's administrative leave?" I had never heard the term before.

"If you'll hold your horses, I'll tell you," he stated impatiently and cleared his throat. "There is a statute that allows only the governor to release an offender on administrative leave. Apparently our governor allowed Mr. Robert "Buck" Roller to take a leave of absence. Now the governor would like him back in prison, and that's where you come in. You need to go find him."

I knew Mr. Kleen wasn't telling me the whole story, but he probably didn't have the whole story either. In my twenty-one years on the job, I had never heard of a leave of absence from prison. Mr. Kleen assured me that he wasn't joking and that Mr. Roller needed to be picked up ASAP.

"Not a problem, just fax the warrant over, and I'll go get him." Now leaning on my desk, I started taking notes.

"There is no warrant and according to our general council, you don't need one. Our council spoke to the attorney general, and they believe this is the best way to handle the situation."

Of course, *they* would think that arresting a man without a warrant would be the best plan of action. They wouldn't be held liable for a false arrest and detention. I felt trapped.

"Why not just call the local police department or sheriff?" I blurted out.

"Well ... because," he was stalling now and not very gracefully. "Politically we need to keep this thing quiet. Nobody said arrest him, just find him and give him a ride back to prison."

"And what if he doesn't want the free cab ride?" Mr. Kleen didn't appreciate my sarcasm. I could hear him tapping a pencil on his desk.

"Then you arrest him."

"Arrest him for what?"

"Look, chances are he'll go with you. He got a break and must know the governor, or he wouldn't be at home now. I'll fax you his address and anything else the prison has on him. Try your best to get him today. Any questions?"

I had lots of questions, but I knew Mr. Kleen was running out of patience. If I didn't agree to take the assignment, I would never find out why Mr. Roller needed to be picked up and transported in secrecy. I also appreciated the confidence, albeit fading confidence my boss had in me.

"Look," he said, "Take Claude or someone else in the office with you but just make sure you keep this quiet. Remember that's why we're doing this. We're state, and we won't have the same control of being discreet if we allow the county officials to know about this."

"I'll do my best, and if I can find Claude, I'll take him with me." The notes on my desk read, "No Warrant…arrest anyways…take to jail…FIND CLAUDE!"

"Got to go now, call me as soon as you have him deposited," and with that, the big boss disconnected.

Like a child on Christmas morning, I waited in anticipation for the faxed information. When it arrived, I started going through the old file material in the office. The sections of the desk I had cleaned only moments before were now covered in papers. Finally, I found a pre-sentence report completed on Mr. Roller approximately four years ago.

Before he was arrested for three counts of Murder in the Second Degree, Mr. Robert "Buck" Roller had no prior record. He was fifty-four years old, married with two grown children, and owned more than 6,000 acres of farm land in various parts of the state. His reported income for the year preceding the pre-sentence report was a net $2.5 million.

"Damn!" I covered my mouth so that nothing else could escape. In silence, I thought: "$2.5 million and a new governor: There's the connection. The governor is the state's first Republican governor since statehood, and I bet Mr. Roller was a Republican or at least a Republican want-to-be."

Returning to the files ... Mr. Roller had graduated with an agricultural science degree from a state university. In addition, since our statue was fifty years old and had never been revised, the report included superfluous information related to Mr. Roller's membership with any civic organizations and church or religious affiliations that I had to page through. Every time I conducted a pre-sentence investigation, I always made a mental note to submit to the suggestion box a proposed statute change regarding this requirement. Since I had a list started, I added the thought right after "FIND CLAUDE!"

According to the information in the rest of the file, Mr. Roller was a saint prior to committing the three murders. He paid quarterly taxes and had never been delinquent. He didn't have a traffic record, criminal history, or criminal tendencies. Furthermore his DD214 attached to the investigation indicated a spotless military record. In fact, he served three years in the Marine Corps, one year of which was in Vietnam on and around the DMZ, or demilitarized zone.

I skimmed the military documents and finally skipped to the official version of the crime:

"On the fifth day of September in the year 1999, one Robert "Buck" Roller did commit the act of murder in the second degree with forethought and felonious intent to take the lives of John Williams, Bob Williams, and Harless Williams. The aforementioned act occurred in self-defense but with pre-meditation and malice."

The official version also included Mr. Roller's weapon, a Winchester .30-.30 caliber, scoped rifle. After reading the official version, I still couldn't visualize the crime. When I found the state bureau of investigation report, I started to understand. Mr. Roller apparently was a strict and violent disciplinarian. Occasionally, he physically abused his wife, bruising her face and back on three separate accounts. On one occasion, he beat her enough that she called her seventy-eight year old father, John Williams, for assistance.

According to the crime scene investigators report, the elder Williams asked his daughter to put her husband on the phone. Mr. Williams and Mr. Roller argued until Mr. Roller slammed the phone across his wife's face and told her they would soon have visitors. Allegedly, he also told her old man Williams threatened to kill him and was on his way to their house with her two brothers. Then, Mr. Roller locked his wife in a closet and retrieved his rifle from the gun rack in the back of his pickup. He waited ten minutes before the three men arrived. The report indicated that the Roller's home had a private drive, extending 250 yards from the main yard. Mr. Roller, waiting with his gun cocked and loaded, rested the barrel across the hood of his pickup. Mr. Williams and his two sons entered the Roller driveway in a crimson farm truck. At this point, Mr. Roller fired three shots, killing Mr. Williams and his two sons as they drove toward the house. After the gunfire, Mr. Roller released his wife from captivity and called 911. When the investigators arrived, they didn't find any weapons on the Williams's bodies or in the vehicle.

"What a tragedy," I thought to myself.

When Mr. Roller was arrested and brought to trial, he was accused of one count of Murder in the First Degree, which resulted in a hung jury. In the subsequent second trial, he still wasn't convicted; another hung jury occurred. The record indicated that the attorney for the prosecution still couldn't prove premeditation. Finally, for the third trial, the official charge was changed to Murder in the Second Degree, which didn't require the prosecutor to prove premeditation, and Mr. Roller was convicted and subsequently sentenced to life in prison for the killing of the elder Mr. Williams.

The other two counts for killing the sons were never tried. There is no statute of limitations on Murder II and documentation in the file indicated that the prosecutor intended to try the other two counts if and when Mr. Roller ever got out of prison.

From the case file and the investigator's notes, I decided the trial for the murder of the two sons never occurred because the county in which the crime happened was poor. Prosecuting one count three times probably exhausted three years worth of their funding. Also, in the state, a life sentence was calculated as 45 years, and parole eligibility started at one third of life. Mr. Roller would have to serve fifteen years, or be 69 years old before a parole review. Mr. Roller appealed the verdict, lost the appeal, and started his prison sentence.

After all of the formal accounts, I had to take a break. I walked down the hall and readied my coffee cup for my morning's dose of caffeine. With my liquid breakfast in hand, I took a second glance at the file. As I leafed through the file information, I noticed the Defendant's Version of the Offense. Such a statement wasn't unusual, especially if the offender could read and write; however, I couldn't believe that I had missed it earlier. In his own words, Mr. Roller wrote;

"I do not remember much. My wife and I had an argument concerning what to cook for supper. She got mad and called her father to come get her. I took the phone and told John everything was alright, and he did not need to interfere with our life. My wife and I had been married for 27 years, and I figured it was about time he butted out of our business. He threatened me. Said he was bringing his two sons over to teach me a lesson in manners. They are all bigger than me and compared to the sons, I am an old man."

I tried to picture Mr. Roller. Would I need more than Claude to help me? Erasing the picture of a large, buff, and angry man from my head, I continued reading.

"I feared for my life because like everyone else in the county, we all had guns. I saw them turn down my driveway and shot them."

"Simple enough," I thought. "This should be a piece of cake."

This was a domestic disturbance resulting in murder. My experience as a probation officer taught me clients convicted of these types of crimes seldom recidivate. In fact, if the client's domestic anger was directed at someone who is now deceased, then there wasn't much chance of a reoccurrence. Tapping the papers on my desk in order to straighten them, I finally read the last paragraph of Mr. Roller's statement.

"I would have never shot anyone if it had not been for that damn alfalfa. I have been allergic to it all my life. It makes me do things I can't control. Prior to speaking to my father-in-law on the phone that day, I had been baling alfalfa. I should have known better and wore my oxygen mask."

My confidence disappeared; I didn't know the guy was a nut who got high on alfalfa.

The final document in the file, a newspaper article with the title "Prosecutor Sneezes at Alfalfa Defense," must have been included so someone like me four years later could have a good laugh. Well, I was sort of laughing. In the article, several experts who testified for the defense discussed the behavioral affects of allergies.

Apparently, alfalfa was no laughing matter. An expert claimed that the substance was one of the strongest allergenic elements known to man. In addition, he claimed that he could believe and accept alfalfa as the cause of the crime. The more I read the more my nose itched and the more my stomach churned. I had just taken a whiff of my coffee, to get rid of the imaginary alfalfa smell in the air, when Claude returned from court, carrying an apple, a file folder, and a coke.

"I thought you were going to clean the office, not screw it up."

Claude had been an officer in this county for about ten years, and he had been bugging me for about the same amount of time. Since I had the entire

Roller file scattered across the top of my desk, Claude sat the apple on a book-case, in order to pickup the news article, and said, "Hey ... I remember this guy. I think old Jay Smith did a pre-sentence on this crazy loon."

"Crazy or not," I said, "I've a story to tell you."

I told Claude about the call from division office, my assignment that was now *our* assignment, and erased Claude's name from my list. Claude, who enjoyed intrigue, quickly offered to participate.

"No problem, Casey. Let's just call the sheriff and pass this crazy off to them." I rolled my eyes as if he hadn't listened to one bit of my explanation.

"Division says this is a *state* issue, and we are to handle this *without* any outside assistance."

"Oh ... I get it, why didn't you just come out and say it? The governor's pass may be somewhat less than politically correct. Can he even give passes?"

"Done checked it out," I said. "You ready to go retrieve him?"

Claude's eyes sparkled; he felt this would be fun. While he finished his soda, I formulated a plan.

"Alright, all we have to do is go out to the house and tell him the governor has rescinded his pass. He'll come peacefully, if he knows what is good for him, and then we can transport him to the state prison."

I also explained to Claude my theory about violent offenders and their not recidivating in these types of cases. Claude found a half eaten candy bar in his desk. He chewed the nougat and reprimanded me for such a simple and naïve plan.

"Are you insane? That's not a plan. That's suicide. Surely we can come up with something better than that," Claude insisted.

"Then you take a shot at it," I said. He placed the wrapper of the candy bar on *my* desk.

"OK, how does this sound? We call Roller and tell him something like the gov wants us to check on him. Then we tell him he needs to come down to the sheriff's office because our office is closed because of a flood."

I threw the wrapper at his triumphant face.

"Get serious Claude. Remember, *no sheriff!*"

"I am serious. I'm serious about us not going to his house. Let's get him on neutral territory." Claude offered several more scenarios.

The only conceivable plan Claude concocted included not telling Roller the governor was revoking his freedom. Claude wanted to have Roller come to the office to sign an extension of his illustrious pass. I would call Roller and explain what we needed. Once he arrived at the office and I put him at ease utilizing my refined art of gab and persuasion, Claude would enter the office, block the door, and discuss a change of plans. Basically we would arrest Mr. Roller in our office.

"It'll be as easy as baking an apple pie," Claude, who was no baker, optimistically remarked.

Nevertheless, since I couldn't think of a better idea, I called Mr. Roller's phone number retrieved from the old pre-sentence investigation report. As the phone rang the first time, I could feel my heart jump into my throat. I fretted, "What was I going to say to this man?" On the second ring, I twisted my thumb in the phone cord. By the third ring, I was confident and knew exactly what to say.

"Yes, hello, this is Mark Casey down at the probation office. Are you Ms. Roller?"

There was a long silence on the other end of the line. I could here whispers but couldn't make out the words. A deep voice instructed a lighter voice to give him the phone.

"This is Buck Roller," said a voice I wasn't expecting.

"Hello, my name is Mark Casey at the probation office in town. How are you today?" I tried not to sound like a salesman.

"I'm doing just fine young man. How are you?"

"I'm doing fine also and thanks for calling me a young man even though we are close to the same age."

I wanted to sound calm and friendly rather than authoritative. He listened to me but didn't really care.

"Enough small talk Mr. Casey, how can I help you?"

I skipped the details and went right into Claude's plan. Claude watching from the other side of the room pulled out a mint from his pocket.

"I understand you have a temporary pass issued by the governor ... Is that correct?" I asked.

"If you are asking, was I released from prison? The answer is yes."

"I understand your release was based on a pass," I reiterated.

"I wouldn't call it that. I've no documents labeled a pass. As a matter of fact, I've no papers showing my release. Do you have some form of a pass with my name on it?"

I paused and pondered how I should respond to this. I didn't have a pass or any type of official forms authorizing anything. Thinking of a solution, I marked off "no warrant" on my list. With no other options, I retreated to Claude's proposed approach.

"Yes, Mr. Roller, I have some paper work here and that is why I'm calling. It seems this bureaucracy we work in is rather slow and the paper work has just now caught up to you."

Once I said this, I realized Roller could have baited me. What if he did have a pass and was just testing me?

"Mr. Casey, I'm on administrative leave with no expiration date from the prison I was held in. Now, is this the same thing you are describing as a pass?"

"Yes, I think we're talking about the same thing. What I called about concerns securing your signature on the official forms and other paper work. Since I'm the closest state office associated with the Department of Corrections, the honor is mine."

I even sounded convincing to myself. Hell, I even started believing I had a pass for him to sign.

"Mr. Casey, why didn't the prison just mail them to me, or call me back for signing?"

"Ouch," I thought, this guy is going to make me build on this lie. My mother always told me, "Once you tell a lie, you better have a good memory because you'll have to continually embellish that lie or cut your loses and confess the truth."

Since I had a terrible memory, especially when I was uncomfortable, I was always getting spanked as a child. My mother could spot a lie from three fields away. Even with my track record, I decided to call his bluff.

"Look Mr. Roller, I was given an assignment to secure your signature. If you wish to return to prison instead of the convenience of my office, I can create that option for you. Who knows, they might decide to keep you." I couldn't even hear him breathing any more.

"So, what do you want me to do?"

"I would like you to come by the office today, and we can get this over with. What's a good time for you?"

He declined coming to my office until the next day; he claimed that he had to finish baling hay because it was supposed to rain.

"Damn," I thought. "Not only am I going to have to wait until tomorrow and worry about this all night, but he'll probably be high on alfalfa." I decided to push my luck and try for finality today.

"It'd really help me if you could come in today. Tomorrow is really busy for me, and I'll be in and out of the office."

"What's the rush? I could come in anytime next week also. You could come to my farm today if you need it that bad," he insisted. Somehow the conversation had taken a turn toward me and now the decision was mine.

> ***Should I have:***
> A. Told him to forget it and let the governor handle his own
>   screw ups.
> B. Forgotten confidentiality and sent a posse.
> C. Told the truth. Maybe he would run, and it would then become
>   a state police issue.
> D. Sucked it up and waited until the next day.

I paused before answering and looked at Claude who had almost finished an entire roll of mints. He just shrugged his shoulders.

"Why don't we try the first thing in the morning, say around eight," I suggested. Claude gave me the thumbs down.

"Can't do it then but how about 10:30?" he countered.

Before he hung up, I promised to see him the next day, and I gave him directions to the office. Claude moved towards me from the other side of the room, placing his hands on his hips as he walked.

"Tomorrow? That's too much time. He'll probably get cold feet and maybe even run. I thought I taught you better than that."

"Not my problem Claude. If he doesn't show, at least we tried."

Even though the remainder of the day was busy, the thought of the alfalfa-doped man who had already killed three people raked my nerves all day and night. I tossed and turned trying to sleep but slumber evaded me. I got up about 2 a.m. and ate a plate of pasta because an over-dose of carbohydrates always put me to sleep.

It worked, but in my dreams I imagined Roller shooting Claude and me as Roller sped through the parking lot, firing guns at our plate glass office window. Then I pictured Roller as a zombie from *The Night of the Living Dead*. Every time Claude shot him, creamed alfalfa oozed from the wounds. The wounds healed before our eyes and the bullets made him grow larger. By the time we emptied our weapons, he was twenty-feet tall. We had to call in air strikes to finish him off. After the missiles, I awoke, sweating, and my heart thumping in my chest. My pulse raced, and my hair was disheveled.

And to think – I used to get an adrenalin rush out of these types of assignments. When I first joined probation and parole workforce, I disliked dull moments and thrived off of excitement. Now, I just wanted the nightmares to stop and my pulse to slow down.

When I arrived at the office later that morning, I found Claude rearranging the furniture. He was constructing a path for our exit and creating a reduced exit for Roller. While he worked, we agreed upon a chair arrest in order to catch Roller off guard. We didn't know his size or shape, and we wanted to have leverage and speed. In order for Roller to rise from the chair, he would have to expend time and energy lifting his weight from the chair. If he were standing, he could just make a quick lateral motion for the door.

Claude and I paced back and forth as the minutes ticked away. I even answered and visited on the phone. In between client visits, I would stand and peer out the front window.

"Ten o'clock and all's well," joked Claude.

"Thanks Claude, my nerves really needed that."

Linda Lane, secretary to the attorney next door, came in at 10:15. Linda, Claude's favorite woman to flirt with, asked Claude if he had plans for the weekend. They discussed possible restaurants while I grew restless. I didn't want Linda in the room when Mr. Roller arrived, so I motioned for Claude to show Linda the hall. Since he knew we couldn't risk a civilian in the office, Claude took Linda by the arm and led her out the door.

While I waited for Claude to return, I tried to make myself comfortable in my chair, but I couldn't relax. I tapped my fingers on the arm rest until I heard the door creak open. I expected to see Claude standing in the doorway waiting to tell me something cute. However, what I saw was a giant man, 6' 3" and two hundred and sixty pounds, dressed as a giant Elmer Fudd. He had a farm hat, brown and straw, and loose fitting jowls dangling from his face.

"I'm looking for Officer Casey." The giant said, pulling a handkerchief from his pocket and unleashing a massive sneeze into the cloth. First, I flinched, and then I answered while frantically scanning the hallway and office entrance. Claude was nowhere to be found.

"I'm Officer Casey, are you Mr. Roller?" He extended his right hand and continued to use the handkerchief with his left.

"Yes I am. Do you have the papers ready to sign?" I couldn't help but stare at the handkerchief pressed to his nose.

"I've got allergies." He said. I nodded in agreement and prayed he hadn't been shoveling alfalfa. I needed to stall for time. I needed Claude.

"Please have a seat. How are you today?"

Still no Claude. I was surprised how calm my voice sounded. My palms were sweating, and my stomach churning.

"Listen, I'm fine and you're fine, so let's skip the small talk." He said in a nasal tone; his nose was now red from the sneezing and snot. He shoved the used handkerchief in his pocket as he continued. "I'm in kind of a hurry, and I left my girlfriend in the pickup." He reached for the tissues on my desk and shoved a few into his pocket.

"This won't take long," I said. Stalling for time was just one excuse. I thought this was an opportune moment to talk about our new governor.

"You've known the governor for a long time?"

"Not really." He adjusted his hat and sniffled.

"I just thought that administrative leave from prison is pretty unusual. I'm not sure if I've ever seen another one."

"I'm sure there have been many. You must be out of the loop." Not only did he answer my question, but he also insulted me at the same time.

"So, Mr. Roller, how does one go about requesting administrative leave without really knowing the governor?" He took off his hat.

"I don't remember the particulars, but I'm sure Mr. Casey, if you ever find yourself incarcerated, you'll figure it out." Mr. Roller kept staring through me and towards the back exit of the office. "Look, if you don't have the papers ready, I can come back," he said.

Now was the time. I couldn't stall anymore.

Should I have:
A. Said, "I don't have the papers. Please come back later."
B. Said, "Excuse me," while I go next door and kick the shit out of my partner.
C. Gone ahead and told the truth.
D. Told him that I made a mistake; he really needs to go to the prison in order sign the document.

I quickly perused all my options. None of them seemed to fit.

"Mr. Roller, things have changed. The signature for the administrative leave isn't necessary." He readjusted his heavy body in the chair. "Your administrative leave has been revoked, and I'll need to transport you back to prison." He looked calm.

"Does this mean I'm under arrest?"

"No, but it does mean I'll have to detain you and transport you. Based on your security level, I have to put you in handcuffs and a belly chain."

Again, he appeared calm and in fact had stopped twitching and turning in his chair. With his elbows on my desk and stretching his neck toward my face, he stared into my eyes and asked, "Did you know this yesterday?"

"Well, kind of. Sort of. I wasn't sure."

"Well, I didn't expect to be on leave forever. I just didn't think it would be this short. I was told I could stay out until after harvest, and I got my finances in order. You see, even though I was out on bond pending my appeals, I really didn't expect to go to prison. Everyone knows I was innocent. It was self-defense. Now I need to harvest and put my ranch and farm in a trust because a life sentence is a long time. However, I do expect to make parole on my first eligibility date." Even though he was rambling, I appreciated the small talk. Claude still wasn't back.

"I'm glad you understand the situation," I said with a voice of relief.

"I just need to drop my girlfriend off and pack a few items and then I can come back to your office." My somewhat happy face melted into a frown.

"Mr. Roller, you can't go to your vehicle or to your home. You can make a phone call if you like and have your girlfriend bring your allowable belongings to the prison."

My answer didn't appease him; he motioned towards the door.

"Well at least let me go down to my truck and get my deeds and other important documents. I was going to the bank after this visit and it appears that won't be the case." He sneezed again; his eyes now as red as his nose.

"Sorry Mr. Roller, you're going to have to sit here. As a matter of fact, here comes Officer Mendoza now."

Claude came in, looked at his watch, gave that "oh shit time flies" look and shoulder shrug, and then entered the office. He stood four feet from Mr. Roller and his hat.

Eyeing Claude's handcuffs, Mr. Roller said, "Gentlemen, listen, if I can just talk to the governor's people, I'm sure this misunderstanding can be straightened out."

Explaining how Claude would secure him to the chair, I ignored his remarks until he made a final plea for his freedom.

"Look officers, I have a lot of important stuff in my truck and I need to get it out. There might be a little something in there for you guys. If you know what I mean?"

Claude and I looked disgusted, and Mr. Roller looked triumphant.

"No, I'm not sure what you mean," I said.

"I'm sure you know I'm a wealthy man and usually keep some cash on me. All I'm asking for is a day or two to get my affairs in order and that's worth a bunch to me. You look like you're close to retirement and Officer Mendoza just looks like he needs money. It's not like I ain't going back to prison. Just give me two days."

"What do you mean, I look like I could use some money?" asked Claude.

"Just look at the way you are dressed. You certainly aren't a poster boy for GQ."

"Okay Mister, put your hands behind your back," Claude ordered. Claude lunged towards Roller, and Roller bolted towards the door. I had never seen such a big man move so quickly. He was up, sneezing, out the door, and in the hallway before I moved a foot. Claude at least made a grab for him, but he only caught air.

Our office was on the second floor where all offices opened into the walkway. The narrow outdoor corridor ran the length of the store front complex. At each end, a spiral staircase led to the parking lot and pedestrian exit. Claude and I may have been beaten off of the starting line, but we knew the building and gained ground across the walkway. As we passed the glass window, I recalled the dream of alfalfa pouring out of Mr. Roller's body. Then, I thought, we were all moving too fast to make the corner at the stairs.

Claude, in an effort to break off the earlier conversation with Linda, had asked her to buy us a couple of cokes from the corner quick stop. There she was, aiming to please the flirtatious Claude, promenading toward us with cokes in hand. Attempting to not have a head on collision with Linda, Mr. Roller slid into Linda and the wall with the speed of a New York Yankee stealing second. The Astroturf carpet caught Roller's side, clinging to his flesh, scraping his body across the floor. His head hit the iron awning on the stairs. Linda ended up throwing the drinks at the porpoise sliding towards her. She hit him in the head with the diet while the caffeine free went over the staircase banister.

Claude and I were on Roller like stink on shit. Oddly enough, he didn't resist, probably because he hit his head on the railing. Actually, he was apologetic. While I held Mr. Roller to the ground, Claude handcuffed him. As we lifted Roller to his feet, I saw Linda disappearing around the corner in the best one hundred-yard dash she could muster in four-inch heels.

Surprisingly no one was injured. Roller complained about the carpet burns on his knees and arms, and Claude told stories about how he used to run the forty yard dash in high school. After Claude and I secured Roller, we walked him to our car, next to a new truck: Roller's pickup truck.

"Where's the girlfriend?" Claude asked Roller in a smart ass tone. I guessed Claude was still pissed about the GQ remark.

"I came by myself. What're you going to do with my truck?"

"It'll be towed and we'll send you the bill!" Claude smiled when he mentioned the bill.

"I have a lot of money in the car. Can you call my banker to come pick it up?"

"No can do. However, since you have notified us there are valuables in the vehicle, we'll go ahead and inventory the contents so you can sign for them."

Claude stood, holding Roller by the handcuffs. Since I needed the truck keys I took this opportunity to frisk Roller. I found nothing out of the ordinary: car keys, Kleenex, and lint. However, in the car, I found a year's supply of Red Man chewing tobacco, several pocket knives, a loaded shot gun, and, oh yes, $150,000 in cash. I also found an airline ticket for Paris, France, and a picture of an old girlfriend. I showed Mr. Roller the airline ticket and he told me France didn't have an extradition treaty with the United States.

He explained, "I could tell on the phone yesterday, you were probably lying. I played the odds that you weren't but also hedged my bet and decided if I got away, I would leave the country."

To maintain the secrecy Mr. Kleen required, we loaded Roller, the tobacco, and cash in our state car and drove the two hour ride to the prison. I let the prison officials inventory the goods; I simply didn't want to worry about it. Mr. Roller never said a word in the vehicle, but he made plenty of noise, wiping and blowing his nose. When we arrived at the prison, he greeted his fellow inmates, "Hey fellows, I'm back," and stopped sneezing.

I slept well that night, no dreams and no pasta. I rose early the next morning, poured a cup of coffee, and stepped out into the bright sunshine. I was ready for a normal work day. Picking up the Tuesday newspaper off of the damp lawn, I could smell the fresh cut odor of alfalfa. I also saw the allergen highlighted on the front page of the newspaper: "Alfalfa Killer Back in Town."

"Suck," I thought. Hoping I had read the title wrong, I skimmed the article. "According to Linda Lane, who helped two local probation officers in the capture, Roller, did not go peacefully."

My boss was not going to be happy.

"Shit, Linda must've called the police," I postulated. We had forgotten to check on her, and we had neglected to do a debriefing of the incident. The whole ordeal was now in the papers. Walking into the house, I shut the door and placed the newspaper next to my answering machine and its blinking light. One new message. I reluctantly pushed play.

"Casey, Kleen here, what the hell happened yesterday? It's all over the news. I told you secrecy CASEY! Do you know what SECRECY means?" Obviously, I didn't.

Footnote: Mr. Roller was eventually tried and convicted of the other two murder charges. Also, the governor after finishing his term and not seeking re-election was convicted on federal bribery and conspiracy charges. Mr. Roller, as a witness for the government, spoke against the governor.

Chapter Eight
"Family Ties"

Kevin Bryant was an ordinary client, but, then again, he wasn't. He had three children: two pre-teen daughters and a high school football star. Kevin's long arrest and conviction record started when he was his son's age and peaked fifteen years later in his thirties. Now, at the age of fifty, he was trying extremely hard to go straight and remain stable.

He held a steady job and never missed our meetings. Apart from his criminal record and past, Kevin's reliability, truthfulness and the fact that I believed him to be honest made him different from normal parolees. I observed his progress and didn't think he would ever lie to me.

It was difficult for me to trust a client because I had been involved in some form of the criminal justice system for most of my life, if you include ten years in the navy as a military policeman and four years in the Marine Corps doing the same. In addition, after serving dual military terms, I spent the next twenty years as a state police trooper, riding and protecting citizens along our many miles of interstates. For the last five years, I have worked as a probation officer. Either call it professional judgment or just intuition, but I felt like I could tell when a client was being honest. Kevin, without a doubt, was honest.

Kevin's two brothers, both on my caseload, contributed to his unique status. The Bryant family, well known in the city, used to run a third generation restaurant that was known for its spicy barbecue sauce and apple pie. After Kevin's parents died, none of the sons could carry on the family business because all three were in and out of jail.

When the restaurant collapsed, Kevin and his older brother, Melvin, were already Vietnam veterans and convicted felons. Even though Kevin and Melvin had criminal records, the youngest brother, Leroy, was the real trouble maker. He had done time in prison for armed robbery. Incomprehensively, through the good heart of Judge Adams, he recently received an unprecedented third suspended sentence resulting in probation for Unlawful Delivery of Marijuana. He should have gone back to prison, because under state law he was supposed to be ineligible for probation. However, if everyone who was ineligible for probation was off my caseload, I would need to find another job.

Not only was Leroy the bad apple of the family, he was also the hardest to supervise. I waited for the day that his sentence would either be revoked or he would catch a new sentence.

I had no doubt that he was committing new crimes. My friends in the police department and the prosecutor's office drug task force always came up with Leroy's name when arrestees wanted to play "let's make a deal." In other words, some detainees traded information about Leroy's activities for their freedom and/or a suspended sentence, not necessarily a smart exchange. Leroy could be dangerous. He thought he was smarter than everyone else, and if his wits failed him, he resorted to violence.

Several times Kevin had come into the office on reporting days with a facial wound or swollen eye. When asked, he always blamed Leroy. In the usual scenario, Kevin would try to protect Leroy's family from his drunken brother, and Leroy in an intoxicated state would smash Kevin into the wall or some other immovable object. Additionally, if Kevin refused to lend Leroy money, Leroy would inflict further harm on him. Kevin had neither the strength nor the money to stop Leroy's beatings.

The third brother was a totally different story. Melvin drew a monthly disability check resulting from his military service. I was never sure what happened to him, but I knew it had something to do with his time in Vietnam. This guy was crazy. After completing his pre-sentence investigation, I tried to convince the judge and prosecutor to put him on unsupervised probation. However, they thought it would be funny if I had to supervise Melvin. I guess it was funny to everyone but me.

It wasn't that I was afraid of him; it was just the fact that he was totally unpredictable. Even when I prepared his pre-sentence report, he failed to co-operate.

When I went to his house in the middle of August to conduct the investigative interview, he answered the door before I could get up on the porch, wrapped in a trench coat and blanket with a scarf tied around his waist. He had the fireplace blazing and the thermostat at 95 degrees. I was pleased that he wouldn't let me in because I wasn't the polar bear he was expecting. Instead of answering my questions, he told me I had two seconds before he would tell his killer penguins to attack. He promised they would enjoy dining on human flesh and would even consider my liver a delicacy. Melvin, demanding I leave as soon as possible, kept a straight face as he stood there with three feet of mangled beard decorated with Christmas ornaments and an afro wrapped in tissue paper.

Melvin was my first pre-sentence investigation in which I never interviewed the client. I affectionately called the encounter "investigation by proxy." After verifying all the psychotropic medications he was taking and the type of therapy he was receiving, I put all of the information I had gathered, highlighting the incident with the penguins, into the pre-sentence report and recommended unsupervised probation. To my chagrin, the judge ordered me to supervise him in open court and on the record he explained that Melvin needed a probation officer to ensure he stayed on his medication and attended all therapy sessions.

I responded, saying, "Judge, probation should not be the social services or the mental health facility for the community."

The judge just laughed and advised me the Veteran's Hospital and the County Health Department needed my years of experience on this one.

At the time, none of this made sense to me. All Melvin did was break into a car at the local Ford dealership and sit in the car all night. So what if Melvin claimed the car was sitting on the exact coordinates Captain Kirk and Mr. Spock gave him? He was simply waiting for Scotty to beam him up. I couldn't get anyone to confirm or deny he was on or off his medication that night.

Anyway, in my estimation, he needed to pay a little restitution and do some community service instead of being on supervised probation. Once he was placed on probation, I tried to convince my supervisor to allow a risk classification override to an administrative caseload that required little or no personal contact, but to no avail. Melvin just had too many needs. In the end, I was supervising the whole Bryant family.

If the Bryants were the family on probation, then the Stovers were the family crime wave from the other side of the tracks. I had five Stover family members on my caseload including brothers Steve and Rodney Stover, the hardcore desperados.

Steve was the oldest and had been to prison on three occasions for the same crime: armed robbery. I supervised his probated portion of a split sentence. He was a thirty-something skinny man, had the mentality of a child, was hooked on every drug he could find and had been caught for every crime he had committed. After his last armed robbery, the cops caught him because he cut two eye holes in the back of his t-shirt and then pulled it over his head like a ski mask. With his eyes peering through the holes, he hid his identity and robbed the store. Since he was a known convict and was seen in the area of the robbery, the cops wanted to bring him into the station for questioning. When they picked him up, he was wearing a t-shirt with eye holes cut in the back. Oh yes, the t-shirt also had the lettering "S-T-E-V-E" on it. He apparently thought he had turned the shirt wrong-side-out before he robbed the gas station.

Steve's brother, Rodney, was in his late twenties, had been in prison twice, and had spent most of his adolescent years in juvenile detention centers. He was a glue and paint sniffer, probably since kindergarten. Compared to Rodney, Steve was an Einstein. Rodney had long ago killed the majority of his brain cells. Now he walked around like a catatonic from *One Flew Over the Cuckoo's Nest,* only occasionally having a moment of clarity.

In an instance of semi-coherence, he committed his latest crime. He walked up to a young man who was fixing a flat on his car and raped him. When Rodney was arraigned, he told the judge he was having a flashback and thought he was in prison. I wrote a violation report recommending revocation. Since a family that crimes together-stays together, the family pooled their money and bailed him out. Both the new charge and revocation were pending. In the meantime, Rodney was out on bond.

Although the brothers were small in stature, about five feet eight inches with Steven being a little taller, the other hoodlums on the streets feared the Stover family. Rodney's and Steve's father was on probation for Concealing Stolen Property, their grandfather was on probation for Burglary II, and a first cousin was on probation for Assault and Battery. In my estimation, the cousin had the best chance to successfully complete probation. He was young with no prior record and appeared to be embarrassed by his extended family and the name of Stover. In addition, the cousin had followed one of my treatment referrals. I made many attempts to get Rodney and Steve into treatment, but I now felt they were a lost cause.

The Stovers, with their confederate flag hanging from the front porch, lived together along with Grandma Stover in a three-bedroom, white clapboard house about twenty yards from the railroad tracks. There was also a dilapidated goose neck trailer in the back yard used as a family-operated drunk tank or detoxication center. I found Rodney and Steve locked up there on several occasions during my home visits. Grandma Stover practiced her own form of correction when her boys got too drunk for her to handle.

The Stover camp was just a few blocks from the old Bryant home where Kevin Bryant lived. Melvin Bryant lived in a rented house down the street and Leroy Bryant and his family rotated between the two brothers' homes. I was sure Kevin was paying for most of the costs associated with maintaining both homes.

"Mr. Hanes, it's the same every month. Just trying to feed my family and keep a dry roof over their heads. I'm still working on the city garbage crew and, no, I haven't been arrested." Kevin finished his report and, as he always did, handed me a money order for his $40 per month probation fee.

"Mr. Hanes, I'm a little short on cash this month. Do you think I could borrow $50 until payday?"

I looked at Kevin in his garbage collector's uniform, a one-piece, heavy cotton gray jump suit, all torn, tattered, and stained with the city's garbage and, as usual, responded, "No." I paused before I went on because Kevin looked worried. "You know loaning money to clients is against policy."

"Yes, you've told me before, but I thought I would ask again. You see, I've been sick lately and I've started to lose weight, and I don't have enough cash to pay my deductible at the hospital. They've been running some tests and want to run some more, but I had to stop because I don't have enough cash. Besides, I can't take off work anymore or I'll get fired."

Again, I just knew Kevin was telling the truth. He had asked for money before during his three years on probation but not often. Kevin and I had gone through the same routine at least five times. We both knew the game. He would ask for a loan, and I would say, "No." Later he would find an unmarked envelope, containing the money he needed, in his mail box. A few weeks after the drop off, I would find an envelope in my mail slot with my name on it, containing the same amount of cash. Kevin was honest and good for the repayment, but neither of us would acknowledge this clandestine process.

Policy violation or not, it was the right thing to do. When I had a female client who I knew needed help because public assistance didn't provide enough nutrition for her and her baby, she would sometimes find a case of infant formula on her doorstep. I knew about her drunken husband, who made just enough money to reduce her benefits, and I knew about the routine beatings and mishaps. She would leave him on a Friday and return the following Monday because her environment held her hostage.

I would have terminated Kevin's parole early or sent his file to an administrative caseload, if he hadn't scored so high on our risk classification instrument. According to policy, his criminal background forfeited any possible override, making me feel like a hypocrite. On one hand, I had to believe people could change or, at least given the guidance, could change themselves. But, on the other hand, when someone like Kevin changes himself, the bureaucracy wouldn't allow exceptions. I handed the probation fee payment back to Kevin and told him to cash it and use the money for his medical co-payment.

"Mr. Hanes, I couldn't do that," he said. "I pay my obligations and, besides, if I get behind, I'm sure the parole board is just looking for an excuse to revoke me."

"I don't think so. I can waive fees for a few months. They'll understand."

"Nope, ain't going to do it," he responded.

"Have it your way," I said, placing the fee on my desk. I moved on, "If you see those brothers of yours, tell them to get in here. They're late reporting."

Kevin smiled because he knew I didn't want to pay a home visit to Melvin or Leroy; Melvin because I never knew if he was thinking he was in a Star Trek episode or some rendition of *Texas Chain Saw Massacre*...Leroy because he might fancy himself as Pacino's Tony Montana in *Scarface*.

"OK, Mr. Hanes, I will tell them," Kevin offered.

Kevin then left with the same slow walk in which he entered. He focused on the ground as he closed the office door behind him. My mother used to tell me to keep my head high because a bowed head was a sign of low self-esteem. She was always concerned about my self-esteem because my father was an alcoholic, and she prayed his disease wouldn't inflict me.

Kevin Bryant appeared even sicker the next time he reported. He slowly strolled into the waiting room and slouched in the corner chair. He wasn't one to speak or make eye contact with the other waiting clients or with the receptionist. He usually reached for an outdated *Sports Illustrated* and scanned it cover to cover. Sometimes he would ask if he could take it home to finish reading it. I always said, "Yes." He would return it on his next visit, even though I told him to keep it. This time he just sat there trying to hold his head up; he didn't have enough energy to reach for a magazine. I noted his changed demeanor before I greeted him.

"Come in Kevin. How are you today?"

"It's been a tough month," he responded.

"Tougher than usual?"

"Yeah, lots of stuff going on," he said as he staggered into my office, relieved to sit in a chair.

"Want to tell me about it?"

"Not really, it wouldn't make any difference," Kevin replied.

"Sure, that may be true, but give it a try. Sometimes just talking about it helps."

I waited for a response. Kevin carefully reached for a security pen from the twenty or so coffee mug-corralled freebees and giveaways I had collected over the years while reading the engraving on the customized pencil holder, "In Appreciation for Twenty Years of Dedicated Service." He selected the Daffy Duck ball point pen.

"Kevin, did you tell your brothers I needed to see them?"

"I told Melvin, but he wasn't doing too good. He has been off his medication, and I wouldn't go see him if I were you. He's pretty wild these days and acting all crazy again. I called the VA, but they wouldn't come get him. He just sits locked in his house and talks to himself all day. Leroy's been staying at my house, and I told him you needed to see him. But he ain't been around this last week."

He paused and selected another pen from my collection. "Doctor says my white blood count is too low. I need further tests, but they won't do anymore until I make a few more payments. I haven't missed any work yet, but I did get dizzy last week and fell off the back of the garbage truck."

"Does your boss know you are sick?"

"Yeah, but he just reminds me there are dozens of people waiting for me to fall out, so they can have my job. I ain't going to let that happen." Kevin was sick, but he was determined. He was naturally slight in build, but now he was absolutely gaunt looking.

After Kevin left the office and my other clients cleared out, I searched my collection of business cards. I kept a business card on everyone and anyone who might have some connection that might benefit one of my clients. I already knew Kevin was on a veteran's hospital waiting list for outpatient health care, so I didn't bother calling them.

I contacted several non-profit organizations to solicit donations and I called the Department of Human Services and the local Crisis Hotline but to no avail. Then I got lucky and discovered an old business card for the local chapter of the VFW. They told me that their usual assistance was restricted to funeral services and support, but when I mentioned Kevin they recalled his regular attendance at sponsored functions and decided to set up a procedure to collect donations for Kevin's medical needs.

As the autumn induced early darkness approached, I drove to Kevin's to tell him the good news about the VFW and to invite him to join me when I visited Melvin. Also, if Leroy was hanging around Kevin's house, I could make my required visit with him.

It wasn't unusual for me to make field contacts at night because it was easier to make contact with clients during suppertime. New officers seemed to want to make field contact attempts during the day often because they were unfamiliar with the realities of their jobs and clients. Day contacts never made sense to me. The fundamentals of supervision require knowing clients and what better way to know them than to interact with them in their environment?

My approach, needless to say, also had an element of adventure and an aspect of risk. Over the years, I had walked into a precarious situation or two, and, consequently, I had observed drug parties, gang activities, weapon exchanges, and X-rated entertainment. However, with good sense and training I would graciously overcome the situation and survive unharmed and uncontaminated.

Driving across town, I noted the definite and distinct transitional lines between one neighborhood and another. Rather close to Kevin's home, I passed through the "Stover area" of town with its 1930s wood-framed homes. These homes didn't get better with age and probably would never be listed as protected historical property. Old elm and oak trees lining the streets were either dying or dead and the city had no plans to remove or replace them. The once level sidewalks of necessity were now crumbled, broken, and unusable, appearing as if the shifting of a tectonic shelf pushed them skyward creating uneven peaks of concrete every few feet. The streets, once paved, were now sporadically covered with gravel or cheap asphalt in the street department's triaged effort to save money.

In contrast, some Westside neighborhoods developed about the same time as the "Stover sector" received regularly maintained smooth layers of concrete for their sidewalks and newly paved streets. The two neighborhoods received disparate levels of funding and maintenance because politically connected old money still inhabited the Westside of town while the disenfranchised perpetual poor occupied the Stover section.

The Stovers lived toward the end of a decaying landscape where the decomposing met the dying. As I passed their house, Rodney, Steve, and the rest of the family waved. I slowed but didn't stop. Returning their salutation, I pretended to not notice the beers in their hands. Parole regulations forbid clients from consuming alcohol. I, again, had to use common sense. If I violated everyone who drank while on supervision, I would never leave the office because of the paperwork. Furthermore, in this instance, I couldn't by myself take on the Stover family. Also, I reasoned, I didn't believe the Stovers were going to drink and drive because Grandma was there.

The transition from the Stover to the Bryant neighborhood provided yet another distinguishable contrast. Near Kevin's home the houses were smaller and in many cases neater. However, nearly every other home was vacant and boarded up. I crossed the railroad tracks and pulled into Kevin's driveway.

Clarissa, his wife, answered the door and, as always, greeted me with a smile and an invitation to enter. When I walked into the neat, yet sparsely furnished, living room, Kevin Jr., watching football highlights, looked up long enough to indicate that he knew I was there. He was as tall as his father, about six-foot one, but much more muscular. He was always quiet and respectful, but I sensed his passive dislike for the parole system or more specifically resentment for his father having to report to me.

"Officer Hanes, can I get you some ice tea or something to drink?" asked Clarissa. She gave me a quick smile, and with a pleasant disposition, motioned towards the kitchen.

"No thank you Clarissa. I just came by to see Kevin. Is he around somewhere?"

"He's over at Melvin's ... down the street."

I let out a muffled exhale as I thought of having to encounter Melvin. I needed to make a home visit but not necessarily today. I wasn't mentally prepared to fend off the penguins.

"If you think he won't be long, I could wait or come back later."

She shook her head and shrugged her shoulders, indicating that it would be a wait. "You might want to go on over there," she offered. "Melvin had some trouble last night, and Kevin is over there checking on him."

"What kind of trouble?"

"Not really sure," she said. "Sometimes Melvin walks to the Quik Stop or the grocery store. You know he always talks to himself, and sometimes people, they don't understand he really is harmless. Like I mean, sometimes they hear him talking and think he is talking to them, and sometimes people just bother and bully Melvin."

"Do you know what happened this time?"

"Not sure but he got beat up a little."

I thanked her for her time and wished Kevin Jr. good luck during the playoffs. He nodded and kept his eyes glued to the television. As I crossed the yard, Kevin's two young daughters ran in front of me and without skipping a beat said in unison, "Hey Mr. Hanes." They disappeared around the corner of the house.

Melvin's house was close enough for me to walk to; however, since I didn't know a lot of people in the area, I decided to drive. It wasn't that I was afraid to walk through the neighborhood; I just liked to play the percentages. I knew the research, and I knew that most officers were injured by people they didn't know.

I parked in the street in front of Melvin's house. The driveway was covered with growing stalks of prairie grass and occupied by scattered broken glass and leftovers from a garage sale Melvin had five years ago. One of the benefits of a non-affluent neighborhood was the freedom to have yard junk. Melvin's house was an exact square, which reminded me at times of the *Little House on the Prairie*. The porch light wasn't on, and I couldn't see any light coming from inside the house. When I raised my hand to knock on the front door, Kevin opened the door.

Startled I blurted out a logical question, "Did Clarissa call to let you know I was coming?"

"No, I was just leaving. Besides, Melvin doesn't have a phone."

"Must have been serendipity," I said.

"Must've been what?"

"Never mind. Can you stay a minute while I see Melvin? How is he anyway? I heard he was in a fight."

"Melvin doesn't fight. He just gets beat up. Come on in."

He pushed the weather-beaten front door open and motioned for me to come inside. I had never been inside Melvin's house. In fact, I had never gotten past the front porch. Man, it was hot in there. Melvin was keeping the place heated like a sauna. I walked across the dusty, hard-wood floors, creaking and squeaking with every step.

Since Melvin had only a chair, sofa, a kitchen table and no wall decorations, the hollow house echoed my every movement. Each step I took was louder than the previous one. The sofa in the living room had a matted and balled up nylon-cotton blend make-shift slip cover and a large "Roy's Barbeque" ash tray decorating one arm. The fireplace was boarded up with the paint stripped panels from the outside of the house so Melvin couldn't light fires anymore.

Kevin led me into the kitchen, separated from the living room by a solid warped-wood door with a glass door knob. The kitchen floor had been covered with a fading, one-piece role of antique linoleum. The legs of the one chair pushed under the small, yellow-tiled tabled had, over the years, worn through the linoleum and rested on original hard wood flooring. As a matter of fact, the whole kitchen floor covering had numerous worn through patches, making it appear like a three-dimensional world map. The linoleum was the oceans and the hard wood patches were land masses.

Melvin was sitting on the counter top with his legs dangling over the edge, his hands on knees, and his perpendicular back as straight as an arrow. His body was rigid, but his face was one of calm and deep contemplation. He wore a black, wool overcoat with a matching Cossack fur hat. He had a red scarf around his neck. I stared at his dangling feet shod in an ancient pair of orange Converse All Star high tops: untied of course. His beard had in and on it an assortment of blanket fuzz, lint, and other indiscernible particles. He refused to make eye contact with me and began fidgeting with the stove burners, turning them on and off. Melvin had dried blood on his eye brows and on his left hand.

"What happened to you?" I asked. Melvin didn't respond, but Kevin interjected that Melvin had been in a minor scuffle. Melvin, turning the burner off, decided to join the conversation.

"Minor scuffle indeed! I have been accosted by the devil's disciples! They rose from the pits of hell to battle with the wrath of God, but they found me instead!"

Melvin's harsh tone startled Kevin and me.

"Melvin, you know that's not true," Kevin said.

"Oh, but it is. Ecclesiastes writes a man is only measured by his work, and they are doing the work of the devil. Revenge will be mine say the Lord, and I will do the Lord's work."

"Don't pay no attention to him, he's off his medication. He'll be okay," Kevin assured me.

"Who beat him up?" I asked.

"The Stover boys," Kevin replied.

"Get out of my house!" screamed Melvin, as he shook a trembling finger at me. He also made a marching motion with his dangling feet.

"You better go. He doesn't mean anything by it, but you're being here upsets him," Kevin explained.

Kevin walked me to the door, and Melvin pretended to escort a dog around the kitchen. "Sit dog! Sit!"

I ignored Melvin and turned to talk to Kevin. "I really came by to see you.

I called the VFW and worked out some assistance for your medical tests. Your boss should have the details."

Since he was a proud man, I didn't tell him the VFW was taking member donations in order to pay for his tests.

"Thanks man, I appreciate it."

For once in a long time, his face took on some color, and his posture straightened a little. I drove home feeling quite satisfied that I had made a small difference in the world.

At three a.m. the following morning, I had forgotten that I had made a difference.

"Sweetheart, wake up. The phone is ringing. *I said wake-up.*" My wife was talking the same way she always did, but I thought she was screaming.

"Honey, what time is it?" I asked.

"It's about 3 a.m." my wife replied. While I was asking her the time, I grabbed at the phone and knocked the receiver off the hook. As I reached to pick it up, I could hear a voice on the phone trying to yell over the sirens in the background.

"Officer Alexander Hanes?"

"Yes." I was sitting up in bed, and my wife had placed a pillow over her ears.

"This is Detective Sterling. Can you come down to the station? We have a little problem, and your assistance is required."

"What's going on?"

"Quite a bit. We got what appears to be a double homicide and a possible impending suicide."

When he said homicide, I leapt towards my clothes in the closet.

"The looming suicide wants to talk to you. The problem is that he is barricaded in an old house down on Second Street."

"Who is it?"

"Says his name is Kevin Bryant. We looked him up, and he is on your caseload."

"Kevin Bryant? He's one of my better clients."

I had my shirt and pants on and was searching for some shoes.

"Well he went bad on you. Guess he wants to commit suicide now because he just killed Rodney and Steve Stover. We ought to just let him go ahead and do it."

I didn't like his tone. "I'll be right there."

"It might be better if I send a car for you. Get ready and I will have a unit there in five."

I briefly explained to my wife that I would have to go out for awhile because of a possible suicide. I assured her there was no danger, but she got up anyway and walked downstairs to prepare for a sleepless night. I found my shoes and waited in my driveway. Five minutes later a police car arrived. With flaming lights pulsating, we sped away.

While enroute to the station, we were redirected to Second Street and we eventually pulled up in front of Melvin's house. Detective Sterling, a small man in a cheap uncoordinated suit, greeted me.

"Here's the deal, Hanes."

He moved his miniature cigar to the left corner of his mouth and made a conscious effort to speak out of the right side of his lips.

"We found the Stover brothers stabbed to death in the alley behind the Quik Stop on the corner of Fourth and Main. A witness said he saw them hassling crazy Melvin Bryant out front of the store. Melvin was yelling at them about being devils and threatened to slay them. Then one of the other Bryant brothers showed up and chased the Stover's into the alley.

We went to Kevin's house. He ran out the back door, and we chased him here. This damn house is like a fortress. If we could've gotten in, we wouldn't have called you. Kevin heard us trying to get in and threatened to kill himself if we continued. That brings us to you. He wants to talk to you."

He continued to chew on the end of the cigar while he tugged on the sides of his pants, trying to reposition them on his waist.

"Now here's the rules."

I knew the rules. After all, I was a state trooper for twenty years. I mentioned this to Detective Sterling, but he didn't care.

"Just in case you forgot, here's the deal. You won't be able to go in. Wear this vest and don't take any chances. And oh yeah, you don't have to do anything. We can break the front door down and rush him. However, it would be nice for you to give it the old college try. Don't forget he's already murdered two tonight."

"How do I talk to him? I was here early this afternoon, and I know there is no phone." He handed me a small heavy piece of metal.

"Here, use this two-way radio. We dropped the other one down the chimney. Guess old Melvin had that boarded up, too. We heard Kevin removing the boards to get to the radio."

"Is Melvin in there with him?" I asked.

"Don't know. Kevin wouldn't talk to us just wanted to talk to you," Sterling answered.

I took the radio and studied the control knobs. Since I was used to visiting Kevin in a client and officer relationship, I didn't know how to start this conversation. I tried to transport my mind back to my trooper days. How would I address this situation if I were still a uniformed officer? I decided to start in the same manner in which I started every conversation.

"Hey Kevin ... How are you doing?"

"Doing okay now that I turned off all of Melvin's heaters." I could barely hear him through the radio static.

"Well, as you can hear, I'm here as you requested?"

"Thanks man, I really appreciate you coming down here. I know you got other things to do."

"No problem."

There was a long silence on the other end. By now I'd thought of plenty to ask and say to Kevin, but I gave him all the time he needed.

"What's he saying?" asked Detective Sterling. I didn't respond but simply shushed him with my fingers pressed to my lips.

I finally broke the silence. "You still there Kevin?"

"Nowhere to go," he responded. "I'm a little confused right now, and the cops don't seem to have much patience."

I moved a couple of steps to the right so that I could get better reception and hear him through the radio. "What're you confused about?" I said as I moved even further across the yard.

"We could start with why the cops are after me. I didn't do anything."

"I'm not sure that they're accusing you of anything in particular. I understand Rodney and Steve Stover are dead, and you may know what happened to them."

"I didn't kill them, if that's what they think?"

I believed him.

"Nobody is saying you killed them. They just want to ask you some questions. So come on out, and I'll stay with you until this mess gets straightened out."

"Don't think so. I'm a man with a record from the wrong side of the tracks, no one will believe me. I'll go straight to jail."

I mentioned that was always a possibility, but he needed to at least try to talk to the police. He just needed to come out of the house to set the record straight.

"You don't understand!" He yelled.

"What is it I don't understand?"

I waited patiently again for an answer as my mind played out several scenarios of possible creative resolutions.

"Man I'm already dead," Kevin finally said. Again his words were followed by an eerie silence; a silence that emerged from the sounds of police radios and television camera crews. I glared at the flashing lights but couldn't hear any ambient noises.

"What do you mean, you're already dead?" I asked.

"Don't want to talk about it."

"OK, I respect that, but you didn't ask me to come here for my health. *I* can stay out here all night, but I *can't* speak for all these officers. Kevin, just come on out and then we can talk when you're ready."

"I can't come out. They won't understand. I just don't know what to do."

I was about to explain the best course of action when I felt a hand on my shoulder and turned to find Detective Sterling massaging his chin's five o'clock shadow with the palm of his other hand. He was working on another cigar.

"Hanes ... Not making any progress are you?" chided Sterling.

With my patience tested and what I thought was sarcasm in Sterling's voice, I answered, "At least he's talking. Isn't that more progress than you made?"

I quickly took back my tartness and offered a suggestion. "Look, why don't you guys let me go in there. It's just a suicide threat, right?"

"Could be just that, but could be something else." He made a circle in the grass with his foot before he hit me with a classic law enforcement saying. "You've been a cop, the unexpected is what to expect."

"Yes, and I also know this guy. I learned several years ago that being a probation officer gives you opportunities to really get to know these types of guys a great deal more that just busting them on the street and then seeing them in court."

Detective Sterling didn't appreciate my chastising tone. He looked at the ground and shook his head. "I don't want to burst your bubble, but this guy is a loser. I know you know his record. The whole family is convicted felons."

Now Detective Sterling had the tartness. I let it go because ... well, hell I figured it was just street edginess I was hearing; an edginess I obviously had lost. I ignored his comment and made another attempt toward a resolution.

"We've already determined my credentials and your authority in this case, but I'm here and I don't think you want to storm this shack for a suicide threat."

I turned away from Detective Sterling before he could give me an answer.

"Kevin, you still got the radio on?" I asked.

"Yes."

"OK, just checking. I will be right back with you."

"OK."

Sterling wanted to reenter the conversation, so he recaptured his sarcasm. "Got anymore suggestions Hanes?" he asked.

Should I have:

A.   Gone home and let the police figure this out.
B.   Told Kevin I would revoke him unless he came out in five minutes.
C.   Disobeyed the police and walk toward the door.
D.   Kept trying to talk Kevin from outside of the house.

There really weren't many options. I decided to step back into my probation officer role and try to be persuasive and supportive.

"I tell you what detective, if he doesn't invite me in, I'll talk on this radio all night. However, if he invites me in, you let me go."

I instantly ascertained that this new and improved plan with its small element of adventure and chance appealed to Sterling's gambling sense.

"Tell you what I'm going to do Hanes, add a steak dinner if he doesn't invite you in, and we got a deal."

I saw no harm in his silly macho bet and agreed to the deal. Chuckling to himself, Sterling walked away, and I leaned against the patrol car, making myself comfortable and preparing for a long wait.

"Kevin, you okay in there?" I asked.

"Yes and no."

"Would you talk to me if I came in the house?"

"Don't know. I'm a little confused right now."

"You want to give it a try?"

"Sure, come on in." Kevin responded.

Sterling quickly came back to the squad car. He needed to cover his bet.

"Look Hanes, right now this is suicide prevention, understand? If I called it a homicide investigation, which it also is, then I couldn't allow you to go in."

Sterling's former playful tone had changed into one of panic and fear.

"I understand. It will be like our bet, a secret," I said, giving back a dose of nervousness.

Yes, I knew Kevin, but did I know him well enough to trust that he wouldn't hurt me? I didn't really know my first wife until after we were divorced, and she had purged herself of her aggressive habits.   Maybe Kevin was holding in a volcano of anger against the world. Maybe we were both losers.

Kevin heard me walking across the porch to the door. He unlocked the latch and motioned with his hand for me to enter.   I turned sideways and slithered through the gap in the doorway.   After locking the door, Kevin gingerly backed away toward the opposite side of the room. Watching his tired movements, I noticed the two lit burners on the kitchen stove, the only source of light. As Kevin crossed his legs and sat down on the floor, I followed his lead and started to sit on the ground.

"Stop!" Kevin yelled, waving his hands frantically in front of his chest.

"OK, I won't sit if you don't want me to."

It was then that I noticed why he moved across the room the way he did. My left foot was immersed in a pool of dark fluid. The flickering light of the stove uncovered a stream of blood. Following the small tributary, I traced it to its source: a large round pool of blood and a shadowed figure of a man in the fetal position.

"That's Leroy. He's dead," Kevin said in a surprisingly calm voice.

I jumped away from the body but couldn't stop looking at Leroy.

"What happened?"

"It doesn't make any difference," said Kevin.   "He's dead, I'm dead, and Melvin's dead."

"Melvin's dead too?"

"Yes."

This was no time for Kevin to be giving me his customary short answers. I didn't even realize the radio was still in my hand until I felt my knuckles turn white from my pressure grip. I took one step back and then another trying not to smear blood on the floor. Kevin's arms were crossed as he stared straight ahead; through and past me. I could see no weapon in Kevin's possession, and, honestly, his suicide threat was the last thing on my mind. I was conflicted between a sense of survival and a sense of fear. I couldn't go anywhere, but I couldn't stay there. Kevin, stroking his thinning hair, broke my panicked thoughts.

"I got AIDS," he whispered.

I didn't know what to say. Did I hear him right?

"Did you not hear me?" He looked up at me. "I said I got AIDS."

I let out a harsh tunnel of breath, "How do you know?"

"Got the tests results back today. They say I been infected for probably six years, and it's just now showing up. They say my wife needs to be tested next.

She probably got it too."

This was too much for me. I just stood there not knowing what to say. Two dead Stovers, two dead Bryants, and now Kevin had AIDS. We just stayed there in the darkness battling the flickering stove fire and staring through and past each other. What could I say? What could anybody say? My thought processes vacillated between my role as a probation officer and my obligations to the police outside.

"Are they sure?"

"Yeah, they say it was probably from some units of blood I got about seven years ago when I had a bleeding ulcer and didn't know it. I told you I was dying."

"I didn't understand what you were saying." Now that I had part of the puzzle, I needed a few final pieces. "What happened to Leroy?"

"The best I can figure out is the Stover's were jackin' with Melvin down at the store. It's happened before. Melvin's been off his medication again and on a good day he's crazy. They had already taken his money, and Melvin should have just come on home like he always did. But like I said, he was off his medication. He followed them around the corner and probably tried to perform an exorcism or some damn thing, but, anyway, they beat him up some more. I got the call from a dude who said Melvin was in trouble, so I headed on down to the store. When I got there, I found them brothers dead. I panicked when I didn't see Melvin. I assumed Melvin had killed them guys, but he didn't. I came here and found Melvin dead in the back room, and Leroy shot here in the front room."

I looked at Leroy's corpse and took yet another step away from his body.

"Leroy was still alive and before he died he told me he'd killed the Stovers when he came upon them beating Melvin. Melvin ran and Leroy followed him home. He said when he came through the door – Melvin had left it open – Melvin shot him. He called Leroy a white devil as he shoots him. Leroy knew Melvin thought he was a Stover."

Kevin shook his head. We both knew Melvin, and we both knew he was crazy.

"Leroy died in my arms. I found Melvin dead. He had a stab wound under his arm pit. Guess it hit his heart or something. He's dead, you know. One of the Stover's must've got him a good one."

I always thought Kevin was an honest man but was I a fool? The whole situation was unbelievable or at least hard to believe.

"Kevin, the police say you've threatened to kill yourself."

I expected him to say "yes" or, maybe "no." I didn't know why I expected any response; I just needed a response. I had to have a response. Even under this unbelievable stress and tragedy, Kevin was the same man of few words, but had I underestimated him as a man of action. He raised a blue steel revolver, an old model ten Smith and Wesson. I'd recognize that weapon in the dark anytime. I carried one for years. My first reaction was to get the hell out of there, but my second reaction prevailed.

"What are you going to do Kevin?" I asked with a noticeable tremor in my voice.

"How long do you think I got to live, you know with AIDS and all?" He moved the gun in the stove light.

"I don't know. With medicine these days, you could live a long life. Look at Magic Johnson." As soon as I said Magic Johnson, I felt stupid.

"I ain't got the money Magic has." He shook his head in disbelief. After a few seconds, he found a spark of hope. "Without Magic we wouldn't have those innovations you're talking about. Shit, it took one celebrity…not millions of dead Africans, poor people, and gays to bring attention to this shit."

"That's good insight Kevin. You don't want to be another statistic who took the easy way out. Man, it's a blessing to get old and not everybody gets the chance."

"You think they'll think I killed everybody?"

"Maybe, at first. Once they look at everything, get witness statements, check the evidence and stuff like that, you'll be all right."

"I don't know … seems like we could end all this right now."

I watched the weapon flicker in the light. The barrel was getting closer to Kevin's head and was getting farther away from me.

"If you end it now Kevin, not only do you take the coward's way out, you leave an unfulfilled legacy for your children, your wife a widow, and your brother's death story untold."

"You can tell them."

He put his finger on the trigger and closed his eyes. I had to think fast. I had to speak fast.

"But I won't. Kevin, if you kill yourself, I won't tell the truth to anyone." He lowered the gun but only an inch or two.

"You believe what I have told you?"

"Yes."

Yes was all I had to say. Kevin flipped the gun around and handed me the butt of the weapon. With the gun secured in the waist of my jeans, I raised the radio to my mouth and announced we were coming out. Everything was alright.

I watched as Kevin was handcuffed and placed in a squad car. Before I relayed Kevin's version of what happened, I insisted Detective Sterling tape record our conversation. The story was confusing enough, and I only wanted to tell it once while it was still fresh in my mind.

Kevin nodded to me as he was driven away, passing the arriving coroner at the end of the block.

I wouldn't see him again until he was released from jail three months later. He was charged with Conspiracy after the Fact for Manslaughter, and he reported to the probation office as required for the next year until he became too sick to leave his house. He died three months later after our last visit.

Kevin Bryant's funeral was the only memorial service of a client I ever attended. Others had died while under my supervision, but I never felt compelled to attend their services. I had to go to Kevin's in order to explain and understand my respect and attention to him.

Two weeks after the funeral, Kevin Jr. came to my office. He was a college sophomore now and, like his father, he was a man of few words.

"My father said you were a good man. I promised him I'd never be on probation. I promised my father before he died I wouldn't be a convict."

He looked around my office and laid a $50 bill on my desk.

"Dad said you'd know what this is for."

And I did.

Chapter Nine
"Specialize This"

It was with much trepidation that I attended a judicial conference sub-committee on specialty courts. I had had my share of experimentation and the assignment of offenders with unique problems to customized criminal justice processes, and I wasn't looking forward to another offender adventure.

My first experience was about eight years ago when I volunteered to be part of a drug court. Back then, I had been a parole officer for seven years, and throughout that time had a problem with saying, "No." Therefore, my hand reached for the sky when the chief asked, "Who wants to volunteer for a new specialized caseload?" Of course, he picked me ... *my* hand was the *only* one visible above the crowd. I was introduced to drug court as a justice panacea previously initiated to save a Florida jurisdiction from a drug cartel dictator-ship. I couldn't wait to start my new assignment. However, I quickly learned Hillary Clinton, and those before her, were right. It does take a village, or, at least, drug court would make it feel that way.

Hillary was right

Since I came from a rather individualistic probation system, the biggest challenge was learning to work with others. In a way, it was a flashback to grade school where I had to learn to play and share with my fellow classmates. Until drug court, I always worked alone and had a strong belief that only I knew what was best for my clients. I didn't even want duty officers, when I wasn't in the office, to see my clients. I felt any interference would alter my clients' progress towards becoming law abiding citizens. Once I volunteered, I wasn't pleased that I had to share my drug court participants with a team of professionals.

Enabling legislation had been in statute for three years before our system organized and provided an implementation plan. Since I was the voluntary probation officer for the initiative, I had the pleasure of writing the policies and procedures for the court. My assistants, the implementation team, consisted of an assistant prosecutor, special judge, substance abuse counselor, concerned citizen, and employment specialist from the Department of Human Services.

Throughout our encounters, my catchword was "hilarity." As a probation officer I had been wearing all the aforementioned hats, and I could have and had performed all their duties. In other words, I didn't need the implementation team. Furthermore, I had seen this kind of *supervise by committee* before. It failed miserably.

For instance, when my agency attempted a front street faith-based initiative, it didn't last long. Don't get me wrong, I have nothing against religion; I just don't see it as a central part of probation services. A faith-based group we worked with developed a curriculum for female probationers that included ballet classes, ballroom dancing, hair design, and proper table etiquette. No one was forced to worship at the host church, and none of the classes had anything to do with crime issues.

However, the initiative was acceptably trendy, and politicians praised its purported merits. Like good little public servants we obeyed and implemented as we watched the program fade into oblivion. The faith group failed to convert their diverse and street-smart adult probationers into middleclass church-going Stafford wives. After that experience, I viewed all other new and idiosyncratic initiatives with a skeptical eye. Thus, I whole heartedly believed the drug court idea would fail. At times, I wished I hadn't raised my hand.

The first few development and implementation meetings were horrendous. Everyone tried to tell me how to do my job. "Think outside the box," they pleaded. If I heard it once, I heard it a thousand times.

"If I think any further outside the box, you'll have to send out a search party." I told them.

The disagreements and arguments ebbed and flowed through a compounded maze professional turfland until, after weeks of exhaustive meetings and endless rewrites, we approved a set of procedures. The next step, training stakeholders, included yet another expanding group of participants: defense attorneys, treatment providers, probation officers, judges, prosecutors, media, and anyone else who wanted a dose of the new medicine in town.

After everything was in place and after much grumbling on my part, the day of reckoning finally came. I reviewed – I mean the drug court supervision team reviewed – our first potential probationers. We were a "team" that disagreed, fought, labored, and contrived together, but on the day of our first review, we loved each other. We tried to be a team with a common mission, a team based on harmony and consensus that was going to review our potential drug court participants with compassion and authority: *WRONG!*

We couldn't agree on anything. We were like cats and dogs, like vegans and carnivores – hell, we were like a group lawyers arguing over the constitutionality of the right to pursue happiness. Each one of us wanted to exercise our God-given right to object to opinions about or reject candidates for the drug court.

The assistant prosecutor didn't think anyone we interviewed and considered for drug court was appropriate. She felt all of them would benefit from a little prison time. For example, we considered one candidate who had a previous arrest for child molestation but wasn't convicted, and she commented, "He needs to be someone's bitch for awhile." The candidate had even revealed to us he had been strung up on heroin at the time of his arrest and that he didn't know the girl wasn't of legal age, but the assistant prosecutor insisted he should be smacked for that as well.

The Special Judge, previously a rookie police officer, interviewed a 62 year-old man who had been in prison three times, and who he had arrested in Baltimore. The judge and I voted to let this man into the program. For me, the situation was win-win. First, I showed support for the judge, and second, I knew the convicted old man was too far gone to be a problem (I was right, and this man was one of our first graduates).

After six days of screening and screaming, arguing and bickering, we rejected 47 and accepted 35.

"Wow," I thought. "A caseload of *only* 35 and a team to help supervise them. I've died and gone to heaven." But heaven didn't last long.

Between numerous urine tests, critical staff meetings, violation hearings, implementing intermediate sanctions, and treatment provider issues, I wanted to invent a patch to cure me of my volunteer habit.

After a year with as many failures as successes, we had our first graduation ceremony. I had never cried out of joy in my life. However, when a middle-aged black woman – a drug addict since age 12 – stood before the judge, cried and thanked him for allowing her to be off drugs for the first time in her decipherable life, I almost cried. When she asked to sing a poem she had written for the judge to demonstrate her appreciation, I did cry.

Below is the poem she sang:

Lips in my veins fashioned by syringes injected
Cried to me undetected
Begging me to feed some more
The needle was what I adored
Blue haze on when I started
Broken hearts and dearly departed
Selfishness was never the game
Endings are the same

Thank you team, thank you my Lord
Life is what I adore
I wished for heaven but at a needles tip found hell
Bottomless pit no end to this well
Judge, like a beacon of light
Team in hand, we fought the fight
God have mercy, you shared the light

If she would have sung Steppenwolf's *Snow Blind Friend* or Neil Young's *Needle and the Damage Done,* then I surely would have sung along with her. When it was all over and I had participated in my first specialty court graduation, my appetite was insatiable and I hungered for more experiences with tear-jerking outcomes. The drug court experience, though painful and disheartening at times, opened my eyes to new probation possibilities. Don't get me wrong. *I* was still the best officer for my caseload, and I didn't want anyone interacting with my clients, but I had found a new outlet for my abilities.

Tally Wags and Underwear

My next foray into specialized sentencing regimens moved from a court setting to a revolutionized caseload of sex offenders. After several repeat offenders committed high profile sex crimes, my agency rethought our approach to supervising this type of offender.

Prior to the revamped strategy, sex offenders were supervised like any other probationer. They were on generic caseloads with shoplifters, driving under the influence, and property and violent crime offenders. When legislation passed requiring at least one year of mandatory supervision for all sex offenders discharged from prison, our caseloads numbers soared.

Similar to drug court, committees analyzed data and developed policies and procedures. Like my drug offender caseload, I was once again asked to share my specialized caseload with a team. The team consisted of a treatment provider (because all sex offenders were now required to participate in group therapy sessions) and a polygraph examiner specialist (because sex offenders had to submit to quarterly polygraph exams).

The new policy required that sex offenders be supervised at a level reserved for at least medium risk clients and, more often, that of high risk clients. This meant that I had to make at minimum two contacts per month, one of which had to occur at their residence. In addition, the new policies were retroactively implemented for all sex offenders.

I didn't agree with many of the changes and many sex offenders also objected. However, basing caseload supervision requirements on a strong foundation of data and statistics coupled with research on evidence-based practices, the department inundated me with hard to dispute arguments for the change. These needed changes were never more evident than with three offenders I had previously determined were harmless.

Edwin House was on a two-year sentence of probation for Indecent Proposals to a Minor. He didn't qualify for this sentence, but I learned long ago that judges can do just about anything they want. For example, 44 % of my division's caseloads were ineligible for a probated sentence based upon prior convictions.

A judge who did whatever he wanted asked me, "Do you really think a defendant will appeal such a sentence and demand prison instead?"

Another judge tried to sidestep his responsibility to the new legislation by arguing, "I just accept the pleas. If they aren't eligible, the prosecutor needs to do more homework."

Edwin was a little strange. He still wore double knit pants with a wide white belt and white dress shoes reminiscent of the seventies. Also, every time I saw him he was clad in a short-sleeved dress shirt and a tie but he didn't wear a jacket. He sold insurance for a living, was married, and had a young child. He was a college graduate and appeared to be above average intelligence; whatever that means.

Anyway, Edwin reported like clockwork and always had a report typed out and neatly folded with my name on the front page. In addition, he always answered my questions with, "Yes, sir" or "No, sir." Before his conviction, he had no prior record and came from a good home environment. I wasn't surprised when Edwin was classified to receive the lowest level of supervision prior to the sex offender specialization initiative. Until the new approach to supervising sex offenders, I had never made a home visit and had no reason to do so. After the change, I had to make a monthly home visit, and I had to verify his employment with something other than a check stub or other form of written employment verification.

The first time I went to Edwin's home I saw what I expected. He had his home arranged like Ward and June Cleaver's with his wife in a dress cooking supper while he sat in the living room. I kept looking for Wally and the Beaver. Edwin, wearing his tie at home, handed me his monthly report while he shared his discontent with the new supervision changes. He felt as if he was being punished for his good behavior. I told him I understood and reminded him in six months his case would expire, and he could petition the court for an expungement. In an attempt to drown out Edwin's complaining about the increased supervision requirements while setting on his couch, I mentally replayed the *Leave It to Beaver* theme song. Glancing around, I noticed some church literature on the coffee table.

"Hey Edwin," I interrupted, "didn't you tell me once you were an agnostic?"

His eyes grew the size of saucers while he tried to deny my statement. I just nodded my head and picked up the Sunday morning flier from the Crown Heights Baptist Church.

"Oh that," he said. "That's just a brochure some solicitors dropped by the house the other day."

When he went into the kitchen to ask his wife when dinner would be ready, I read the brochure. On the top of page two, I found what Edwin didn't want me to see:

"Edwin House, youth minister, reports Sunday school enrollment is down."

When he returned, I waited to see if Edwin would mention his new employment, but he remained silent, so I played dumb, bid them farewell, and departed.

The next morning I paid a visit to Edwin's church. I met the pastor as he entered the building, but I didn't identify myself.

"I'd like to see Mr. House," I requested of him.

His reply was all the answer I needed, "He doesn't come in until ten."

Lying about employment was a probation violation but not one that would likely result in revocation. Maybe Edwin lied because he was embarrassed, or maybe he lied because he was a pedophile. I couldn't take a chance. Under the new statutes, I needed to have Edwin submit to a mandated polygraph exam. Thus, I scheduled the appointment earlier than I had originally intended, but he never showed and was eventually declared an absconder. Even his wife didn't know where he went.

Thirty days after his disappearance two young boys from the church alleged Edwin had sexual abused them. After obtaining a warrant, the police found Edwin three weeks later. He was subsequently tried, convicted of sexually abusing the two minors and sentenced to a twenty-five year prison sentence. At the trial, I found out that he had been using the church print shop to create fake check stubs and a phony insurance company letterhead.

Even though I thought the new sex offender mandates were over-zealous and I still didn't want to share my clients with others, the rewards reaped from the new statues kept occurring.

Another of my clients was arrested while on supervision for stealing, certainly a lesser offense than the Edwin House incident; however, the client was still considered to have committed a sexually-related crime.

Chuck Roberts worked as an industrial cleanser truck driver. I never really understood what his job entailed until I had to start making visits to his home and verifying his employment. Chuck was on probation for Burglary I, but the crime involved voyeurism – he was really a Peeping Tom.

The cops had numerous reports from his neighborhood of laundry missing from clothes lines and coin operated laundries. Chuck's job required that he service industrial washing machines and replenish laundry supplies. To make a long story short, once I figured out his truck route and made a comparison to the numerous theft reports, he was arrested for stealing the neighborhood laundry.

The piece of information that I possessed that the posse didn't was that I knew there was a sex offender working in the area. When the cops searched his home, they found a hoard of panties stashed in his basement. He even stuffed his mattress with thousands of thongs and made wall coverings with colorful bikini briefs. After Chuck the incident, we invited law enforcement from smaller cities to join our team approach to supervising sex offenders.

The last client story worth mentioning on my second endeavor into the world of specialization is George Walker. Like most of the sex offenders on my caseload, George had a college degree, but, unlike others, he had a diploma in agricultural management from a state university. George was also smarter than the two previously highlighted clients. He retained a lawyer and filed an injunction against his having to submit to polygraph examinations. After Edwin and Chuck, I had become callused and just damn suspicious.

George was a loan officer at a bank. Trust me; I verified this one as soon as the injunction was served. He was on probation for Indecent Exposure. He maintained that he was just urinating on the side of the road when someone saw him and had him arrested.

Unbeknownst to me, there was a chain of convenience stores in the eastern part of the state called Tally Wags. The stores were experiencing a flasher crime wave. One of the area's local newspapers had labeled the flasher who was terrorizing the Tally Wag stores, as the "Wagging Talley Bandit." Their bandit would bring an item from the candy isle to the cashier, and then, when he reached for his money, he instead would pull out his "tally" and wag it at the cashier. The cashier, always a woman, would either scream or go into shock after seeing a penis in lieu of money, and the perpetrator would walk out of the store without paying for the candy.

Since these rural stores didn't have surveillance cameras, the local law enforcement weren't able to catch the perpetrator until one day George got his "tally" caught in his zipper. The cashier called the cops *and* an ambulance. Painfully, George had to have stitches. When I visited him in the county jail prior to his revocation hearing, I told him that he gave a whole new definition to injunction.

The New Assignment

With my experiences in drug court and a specialized sex offender caseload, I wasn't surprised when my supervisor wanted me to help with the new court for driving under the influence (DUI) offenders. I had heard of DUI courts and thought of them as the bastard child of drug courts.

As a matter of fact, isn't driving while drunk a form of drug abuse? I was always taught that alcohol was a drug, so I wondered why they needed specialty courts for an alcohol-abuse related offense. My supervisor explained this was no ordinary DUI court, but one even more specialized. I rolled my eyes and I thought, "Specialize this, and specialize that. Now they've gone and specialized the specialized."

This new and improved specialized court had offenders who were college students as its primary focus. The judicial subcommittee meeting my boss made me attend – I no longer volunteered for crazy assignments – explained how the DUI program would collaborate with the local university and the clients would all be housed in the same dorm. Supposedly this would improve curfew compliance. The committee also explained how the environment would work as a therapeutic community.

"Right," I thought, as the concept was being pitched at me. I remember my college days where beer ran free like the streams in Montana and drugs were as available as chewing tobacco in Texas. This wasn't going to work.

After the meeting, my boss tried to convince me that I was too pessimistic and that I should acquiescently accept the DUI court assignment.

"Sure it'll work Bill," Mr. Sheehy stated.

"No it won't!" I retorted.

"Look, you're Officer Bill. You have the experience to make this work. You are a team player, and this will take a great team effort."

I frowned and shook my head.

"Get someone else," I said. "Get one of the new officers who look like they belong on campus. This will make me feel a 100 years old, being around all those kids. I feel old enough now when probationers come in having just graduated from juvenile to adult."

"Bill, just think about it before you make a decision. This will be a great opportunity for you. You'll be on the cutting edge of your profession, and, besides, think of all the attention you'll get. You might even get promoted."

"I don't want attention, and I damn sure don't want a promotion. I like exactly what I'm doing now."

I didn't want to tell him, but I really enjoyed working with the sex offender caseload and had become quite content dealing with all the perversion. In my agency, if an officer liked something too much or got comfortable with his or her job, the management moved them to another caseload. In addition, I had heard a rumor that the policy might change to limit how many years an officer could supervise a sex offender caseload. I guess management was concerned about officers becoming myopic, tainted, or perverted.

Let an Entrepreneur Decide

Two days later, I was still trying to decide about DUI court. I was in a team meeting early on Tuesday morning when the husband of a client I had on probation for prostitution came barging in.

"I'm going to kick your ass!" he bellowed.

"Excuse me?" responded my startled and protective team supervisor.

I stood up and said, "Hi" to Buddy and asked him if he was having a bad day. Obviously he didn't think I had heard or understood his initial greeting, so he stood there and shouted a few more profanities. Since he made no motions toward me and was obviously drunk, I didn't feel overtly threatened. The other officers, very uncomfortable with the yelling drunk, stood up and prepared to take Buddy down.

"Sarah left my ass!" he yelled and pointed at me. "And it's all your fault, you son of a bitch!"

He was still just standing there in the doorway because he was so drunk he needed the doorway for support. I motioned for my fellow officers to have a seat.

"Buddy, why don't you come back to my office and we can talk about what's wrong with you."

Buddy shuffled behind me as I lead him to my office. Once there he fell into a chair all slumped over. Then he started to cry and sling snot, wiping it on his shirt sleeve. Buddy was an ex-con who had served a lot of time for armed robbery and other violent offenses, but surprisingly he hadn't been caught doing anything wrong in the last ten years. I figured he wasn't committing new crimes because he wasn't smart enough to stay out of trouble.

"Sarah loved me until you convinced her she was so almighty. Now she is too damn good for me. Wants me to take a bath everyday, wants me to stop drinking, and keep a damn job. I got a job. I am *an opfer friggen manure*."

"You're a what, Buddy?" I asked.

"You know. I'm one of those independent businessmen."

"Oh, you're an *entrepreneur*."

"Hell man, that's it."

This turned the tide on the morning's infringement. We then started to talk about Sarah and how it wasn't my fault he was having marriage problems. He agreed Sarah was changing for the better and at least she wasn't hooking anymore. After about an hour, he stopped crying and stopped wiping his snot on my chair. Two more cups of coffee and he was ready to go.

Once Buddy was gone, my fellow officers bombarded me with questioning ridicule. "Why did you let him get away with cussing you out?" and "Why didn't you arrest him for public drunkenness?"

They just wouldn't shut up. I had out grown my co-workers. All of my experience and specialized training placed me at odds with the other officers. The next day I called Mr. Sheehy and accepted DUI court.

Not Again

I was placed in charge of setting up the whole operation. My team included two licensed substance abuse counselors, an assistant prosecutor, a judge, an assistant police chief, several business leaders, and a victim advocate. This team was larger than my drug court team, but everyone's role was more defined.

The newest wrinkle was the victim advocate. She had to find victim impact groups that would allow the college students to attend meetings and have discussions with survivors of drunken driving accidents and family members of deceased accident victims.

We utilized clients who owed community service hours to paint and remodel a three story, turn of the century, dilapidated dorm. We converted the bottom floor into office space and classrooms, and created thirty residential rooms on the remaining upper floors. After two months, we were ready to move the first of our college DUI little darlings into their new digs.

The DUI court was very active while we were renovating. Counting those college clients who were already on probation and retroactively drafted into the program, we had 32 inductees. My sex offender caseload was never below fifty clients, so I figured my new task would be a piece of cake. I had a captive audience living in the same dorm instead of many offenders strung out all over the city and a team to assist me. In addition, this would be a lot better than talking down drunken husbands of ex-prostitutes. I only had to teach classes for six months until the darlings either graduated or went back to court on a violation of probation for further sanctioning.

The day of reckoning finally arrived. Utilizing volunteers and students on work study, the enrollment and checking in process began. I assigned two dorms parents, one to each floor. Their duties were simple: make sure lights went out at ten and make sure everyone was in at curfew.

I placed the female participants on the third floor and the males on the second. I was a little apprehensive about a coed facility. However, the college students were already accustomed to coed dorms. Also, the dorm parents who were hired looked like descendents of Attila the Hun. In fact, I nicknamed them Hun and Attila.

After I checked in each student, I screened each of them to help determine his/her level of substance abuse. Even though they were on probation for an alcohol-related DUI offense, it would be naïve to think they weren't using other drugs. Following my screening, they would receive additional and more specific assessments from their substance abuse counselors. At the end of the process, the victim advocate scheduled the students' appearances at the victim's impact panel, and Hun escorted them to their rooms.

College Clients

I didn't realize how fast my rose colored view of my new assignment would blacken. After completing three intake processes, I looked up from my desk and saw Dinky Speilman: a small young man, five and one half feet tall, and about 125 pounds.

His unwashed shoulder length hair – disheveled and multicolored – exploded from underneath his Pearl Jam stocking cap. His jeans redefined baggy as he kept one hand on a belt loop to keep from flashing me; probably hoping to avoid any misconception that he was doing "crack" – if you know what I mean. He completed his ensemble with a grandfather's fashionable but ragged long-handled shirt.

"Hey dude, like is this like the dorm for alkies?"

"Yes it is," I replied.

"What?"

"YES. THIS IS THE DUI PROJECT!"

"What?"

I reached across the desk and pulled off Mr. Speilman's headphones. Even with the foam rubber ear pieces draped around his neck, I could still hear Jimi Hendrix's fender guitar waling about *Cross Town Traffic.*

Dinky had three arrests for public drunkenness, all leaving bars close to campus. Most recently, he was picked up after failing to negotiate a right turn and crashing into the side of a house. He'd never been in treatment and was in big-time denial.

My next few intakes were fairly average. There were several fraternity boys, binge drinkers, who didn't have the good sense not to drive. A nineteen year-old girl strolled in, and I thought she was forty. She had been drinking alcohol since the age of twelve; her face showed it. Oddly enough, she was on an academic scholarship.

Each of these students came in with shopping cart after shopping cart filled with stuff. By the end of the day, I saw enough guitars to decorate a Hard Rock Café and enough coffee pots to start a Starbucks.

While I marked off clients who had already arrived, I heard a commotion at the front door.

"Shut up, hoe!" yelled the taller girl.

"You're such a whore!" shouted the other girl as she fought for an Alan Iverson jersey.

"Do you ladies have a problem?" I asked as I tried to separate the two girls before they tore the jersey and each other in half.

"I don't have a problem. You got a problem?" The shorter one cocked her head as she looked at me.

I immediately went on the defensive. They were adult probationers, but obliviously not as mature as my generation at this age, I selectively decided. I couldn't remember if this was the "Y" or "X" generation. Maybe we had moved onto the "Z" generation and would soon start over with the alphabet.

"Ladies, can I have your names please? Have you reported in yet?" I asked as I perused my check-in list. The taller girl let go of the tautly stretched jersey and the second girl stumbled and fell backward into the wall, bruised but pleased to have the shirt in her hand.

"I'm Sharita," said the girl still on her feet.

"My name is Shakesha, Shakesha White, and who wants to know?" said the other girl while she picked herself off the floor.

"Well, that's a good start. I assume you ladies are here for a little rest and relaxation in our DUI court program."

"Yeah, that's right. We've been uprooted and moved across campus from our sorority sisters into this dump," Shakesha responded as she put the shirt over her shoulder and pointed out the lobby.

"Come right this way ladies, and we'll get you enrolled."

Shakesha, the obvious leader, stubbornly followed me with Sharita trailing behind to the admissions desk. After I took my chair behind the table, I introduced myself to the two rays of sunshine.

"My name is Bill Stewart, and I'll be your probation officer and host while at our resort." They both got a small kick out of my dry sense of humor; I could see some of their defenses drop.

Sharita reached out and shook my hand, curtsied, and said, "I'm Ms. Brown, Ms. Sharita Brown."

Shakesha told me that she and Sharita liked to party like everyone else, but they got caught and thrown into "this hell hole."

"Everyone drinks and drives around here," Shakesha informed me. "Haven't you ever been drinking then drive somewhere?" she asked.

In keeping with my drug court training on being up front and honest I answered, "Yes, but I wasn't drunk."

"I wasn't drunk either and that's why I refused to take the blood or breath test at my last incident. I knew them machines would be fixed. They got my number. The police just follow me around all the time until they set me up."

I looked to Sharita for relief, hoping she would say something about her arrest. I could tell from her facial expressions that her friend embarrassed her. Shakesha continued with her litany of "poor me's." After a few moments I interrupted.

"Let's get this straight. You refused the tests, and that's why you pled guilty and are with us here today?"

"I pled guilty 'cause I ain't got the money to prove my innocence."

She was going to be a tough case. Getting succinct information out of Shakesha was a hopeless task. She inflated every answer and acted like a victim on every topic. She went from describing her drunken driving case to telling me her family history. Her father spent time in prison many years ago and now worked as a plumber. Her mother was a nurse at the veteran's hospital, and Shakesha got expelled from her high school her senior year. Eventually, she obtained her GED, and with the assistance of her church and several grants and loans she was now a third semester freshman.

Sharita's intake went much more smoothly. She was an inappropriate designated driver for several girls in her sorority. I suspect this included Shakesha. Her grandparents raised her after her mother died when she was three and her father deserted her. She said her father, now remarried with three kids, occasionally drops some change on her but not enough to pay for college. In order to pay the rent, she worked at the local video store and sold Avon products around campus. It was apparent to me Sharita was a follower and was attracted to Shakesha for her strength and spunk. Nevertheless, it was a volatile friendship.

When nearly all the students were checked in, Stoney Johnson arrived.

"Stoney Johnson is the name." I looked up from writing my summary on the two Shas – Sharita and Shakesha.

"Is that your real name?" I asked.

"Sure is."

"And why are you with us Mr. Johnson?"

"I'm here because I'm a drunk." I looked at this young man with his cowboy hat, tight shirt and jeans, roper boots and bandana tied around his neck, and thought, "Is this for real?"

"So you're a drunk."

"Sure am."

"Are you a practicing drunk?"

He looked at my like I was stupid. "Is there any other type of drunk?"

He paused and sat on top of the admissions desk. "I'm here, sir, for you to get me sober. I'm already clean. Get it, that's funny, huh?" I couldn't believe this kid; he had to be drunk. "Let's get the healin' started!" He raised his hands in the air, jumped off of the table, and pranced around in a little circle.

"That's pretty funny. Have you been drinking today?"

"As a matter of fact, I've had a few beers, but hey, look at me, I'm not driving."

He ran around in a little circle as he pretended to drive a car. When he finally got dizzy, he slowed down and tried to get Hun to dance with him. "You're one hot momma, baby." Hun didn't appreciate her dance partner and returned him to the table. Needless to say, Stoney was the first student of the day to provide me with a urine sample for analysis (UA).

"Mr. Johnson, follow me please."

"Do I get to pee in a cup?" He seemed excited, clasping his hands together like a two-year-old about to go to McDonald's for a happy meal.

"I think we'll do a breathalyzer and a pee. What do you want to do first?"

"I need to pee like a racehorse on crack. Can we do that first?"

"Sure we can."

I handed him a specimen cup and stood in the door way of the men's room while he let it flow ... and flow ... and flow. Austin Powers had nothing on this man. Since I had forgotten to tell him I only needed a couple of ounces, he handed me an overflowing cup of pungent, yellow warmth. When we turned to take the breathalyzer, he pretended to puff on a cigarette and then proceeded to blow spit on the instrument. The breathalyzer indicated a .06 alcohol level, but his urine analysis came back clear of any drugs.

Stoney was all too happy about the results. "Dude, a .06? That's pretty good. Don't I get an award or something for that?"

After a brief dance of joy, he settled down on the corner bench and placed his hat over his eyes. Within minutes, I could hear him snoring a playful tune. I called my team together, and we decided to place Mr. Johnson's room next to Mr. Attila. Furthermore, we grounded Stoney to the immediate vicinity except for the hours he attended college classes. One more drinking incident and he would be immediately referred to the court for revocation of his probation.

My final intake for the day was Jimmy Cohn, a classic Joe College. He had looked like he had graduated from GAP fashion school and was now pursuing a graduate degree from Abercrombie and Finch. His parents, a lawyer and a pediatrician, kept him in the latest styles and trends. Since he had such a wealthy family, I wondered why he was here at a state university, but my wondering ceased once I started questioning him. To put it bluntly, this young man was nearly brain dead. He had been drinking and doing more than alcohol for many years. Occasionally, during the intake interview, he would unintentionally slur his speech, yet at other times, he had a normal, controlled voice. After listening to the fluctuations, I decided to do a UA on him. I was positive he was high, but the onsite drug testing cup didn't detect any toxic substances. The test searched for five common drugs; apparently, Jimmy wasn't just a common drug user.

The Schedule

Our workday started around 2 in the afternoon. The client students had to schedule all their classes in the morning; therefore, my little rascals started to file in about ten minutes after two. The daily routine went as follows:

After their afternoon check-in, orientation and cognitive change classes with me until 4 p.m., they were allowed a short break and then they participated in substance abuse group therapy. Next was another break, and then dinner followed by individual counseling sessions and scheduled victim impact seminars. Three evenings a week a victim advocate, Sally Hayes, would discuss tragic drunken driver related accidents and their consequences. They would also have to watch films on this topic, and once per quarter attend a live victims impact panel.

The rigorous schedule and the fact that the students couldn't leave the dorm without a pass signed by two team members kept the students from having enough time to get into much trouble. However, this didn't keep them from whining and carrying on. Every night Shakesha would stand at the front door to the dorms, call everyone a whore, and complain about her imprisonment.

"Sharita, this sucks! They're keeping me in here like a fool. I ain't done nothing wrong."

"I know Shakesha; I know."

"They're nothing but a bunch of whores."

"I know Shakesha; I know."

After about ten minutes, Sharita would get tired of listening to Shakesha, and Shakesha would get tired of Sharita agreeing with her. They only fought once over their respective views of their quasi-imprisonment. They just got confused and went to bed most of the time.

An hour into my first class, it was obvious that I needed to rewrite and alter my lesson plans. With the exception of Jimmy Cohn, these clients were much smarter, in a deceptive and deviant way, than my average caseload. They were trickier and full of sass.

For every topic I introduced, a debate full of righteous indignation and social politics ensued. After the first debate, the topic of which was how the system only caught drunken teenagers, I decided to let them run with the heated dialogue and contentious discussion. I wanted them to bond, become a team, and assist each other throughout the program. "NOT!" I was just having a hard time controlling them.

As expected, Shakesha tried to dominate with a vociferously deflective style of communication. In other words, she repelled any and all inferences that would remotely suggest that, maybe, just maybe, she had made some bad choices that led her to her current situation. Heaven forbid she may have a substance abuse problem.

Stoney thought everything was funny and once explained that it was his destiny to drink and have a good time. His father did it and his father's father did it. It was the cowboy way.

Dinky Speilman said his drinking was situational and just a passing phase he was going through. Sharita was attentive and raised her hand for permission each time she wished to engage in the conversation, or, more appropriately defined, the verbal riot. Jimmy Cohn just looked around dazed and confused.

After several chaotic classes, I took them through a self-evaluation process. I asked them about their expectations for the class and their lives and how we could best meet their goals. Based upon their answers, I redirected the class and utilized many of the cognitive thinking exercises in their workbooks. I incorporated ways to positively reinforce their participation and progress. However, I didn't include Stoney's recommendation for a six pack of Coors for each completed week.

Several weeks passed, and I could tell my changed approach was working. The clients were in a routine and no one had tested positive for alcohol or drugs with the exception of Stoney on the first day.

Shakesha was still in denial and became the self-appointed person in charge. Meanwhile, Sharita was the most respected.

Sharita had vomited during her attendance at a live victim impact panel. She told me the testimonials from parents who had lost their children to drunken drivers and the films of accident victims were just too much for her. I suspected she didn't have a deep-rooted alcohol problem. With some improved self-confidence and maturity, I could picture her getting beyond her current problems and never appearing on anyone's caseload in the future.

Dinky made progress and even convinced me to buy a Pearl Jam CD. Jimmy Cohn, on the other hand, was tested for drugs everyday. I just knew he was using, but all the tests came up negative.

Stoney had even lessened his bravado about drinking and how it was his destiny. One day, I had explained heredity and environment to him. After two days to sleep on it, he came to class and announced, "I'm going to kick heredity in the ass. I'm going to change my destiny!"

No one understood exactly what he meant, but he mumbled something about cloning, country music, and hydrogen cells. We enjoyed his victory dance.

Furthermore, we learned that Stoney was an astro-physics major, whatever that means.

Yellow Polka Dot Bikini

Smelling a strong odor of coco butter, I turned from my computer to see who had entered my office. There sitting on the edge of my desk was Cindy, the quietest member of my class. If I had had to pick one client who probably didn't need this program, it would have been Cindy Dare.

Cindy readjusted her position, with her legs crossed and her hands clasped together across her knees. I expected clothes, but I saw nothing more than a bikini. She appeared to be either sweating from head to toe or had over applied her Coppertone ... or both. In any case, beads of gelatinous moisture were leisurely slaloming down her neck, chest, and stomach.

"Mr. Stewart, can I have a pass for this evening?" she requested in the sweetest voice I had ever heard.

Before I answered her question, I asked a couple of my own, "Cindy, what have you been doing, and why are you in my office dressed like that?"

"Mr. Stewart, I know I'm not really dressed. I was just out catching some rays. See?"

She stood up, turned around and pulled the back of her bikini bottoms down just enough to reveal her tan line. I could care less about her tan line; I was worried about my desk covered in oil. Plus, the large mystical dragon tattoo crawling down her back looked like it was going to jump onto my desk.

I came to my senses and noticed that she had closed the door when she entered the room. I always kept the door open, even when I counseled clients, because I believed it was a good protective habit for probation officers to practice.

"Ms. Dare, please have a chair and open the door before you sit down." She showed her reluctance with a look of disgust and an irritated walk.

"Now, why do you need a pass?"

"I need to apply for a job and they're holding the interviews are at the Holiday Inn tonight."

"What kind of job has interviews at the Holiday Inn on a Tuesday night?"

"It's a modeling job. They're having interviews tonight only and I just *have* to go."

She rose from her chair and leaned over my desk, placing her elbows on a container holding Jimmy's last drug test.

"Ms. Dare, please sit back down."

She flicked her hair to the other side of her face and obeyed my command. I was not messing with her.

"Now," I continued, "if you'll give me the phone number of this place, I'll call and verify your interview. If everything checks out, there'll be no problem with giving you a pass."

"Well, just forget it," she said, changing her seductress demeanor into one of Shakesha's evil twin. "I don't want the damn job anyway."

"If that's the way you want it, I guess this conversation is over."

Hearing this she stormed out of the office, leaving behind a perfectly good chair permanently stained with sun tan oil.

I walked to the door and looked down the hallway to ensure she had left and wasn't trying to con one of the other team members. As I looked through the front door, I saw Jimmy Cohn get out of a car and place a clear bag in his pocket. I greeted him at the door and asked him to pull-out his pockets. After padding him down and searching his pockets, I found nothing on his person. Then I gave him an UA and once again the test came back negative. Jimmy's smile said "I beat you again" as well as "I *am* using."

I knew he was taking drugs, I knew that he had just taken something, but I couldn't figure out what it was or how to find it. I had watched him decanter the specimen every time. The last few times I had even made him hold a mirror in front of him, so I could actually see him urinate into the specimen cup. Who says probation work isn't glamorous? All the other clients knew he was using and knew I was trying my hardest to catch the little scalawag. I knew someone knew how he was doing it, but like a code of silence, no one was forthcoming with any information.

The next day I received a call from Mr. Sheehy. He opened with the usual pleasantries with compliments about all the good stuff he was hearing about the program and how the presiding judge and university president were very happy with us. He ended on a serious note.

"Oh, by the way, Bill, Internal Affairs should be around to talk to you later today."

"Internal Affairs? What do they want?"

"It seems one of your clients has filed a sexual harassment complaint against you?"

I knew who. "Cindy Dare?"

"Yes, that's right. She claims you asked her for sexual favors in exchange for a night pass."

I rolled my eyes so far into my head that I was surveying my frontal lobes.

"Mr. Sheehy, you know this isn't true."

"She also claims that when she tried to leave, you pulled the back of her pants down to see her tattoo."

"My god! The woman is crazy! I guess I made a mistake by not immediately running her out of my office when she came in with that damn bikini on. Guess I'll know better next time. Mr. Sheehy, an allegation like this isn't good for the program and I don't want to wait around and have internal affairs in here stirring things up. Let's just cut to the chase. Polygraph both of us today and let's put this allegation to the ultimate test."

Mr. Sheehy agreed and by the end of the day the mess was over. I passed my polygraph examination with flying colors, and Ms. Cindy Dare refused to submit to the procedure. When a team counselor questioned her, Ms. Dare admitted she fabricated the story. She attempted an apology. However, it sure didn't feel sincere. After this encounter with Ms. Dare, I vowed to never be alone again with a client under any circumstances. So, when Sharita asked to talk to me, I met her in the hall.

"Mr. Stewart, I have a conflict, and I'm not sure what to do?" I could tell she was troubled, so I invited her outside for a walk in the fresh morning air.

"What's the matter Sharita?"

She twirled her hair and wouldn't make eye contact as she replied, "I don't want to be a snitch or nothing like that, but I know something you should know? I'm just not sure I can say anything."

"Sharita, if, whatever it is, bothers you, then you should talk to someone. It doesn't have to be me. You can talk to any member of the team."

"I know, but I see you trying so hard to make this program work, and I wouldn't want anyone to screw it up for you." I tried to find something to say, but Sharita filled the silence. "I need to go to class now."

I was feeling somewhat guilty because my incident with Cindy created a barrier of mistrust for me with my other clients. Sharita had walked about twenty yards away when she turned and yelled, "Check his arm pits."

Check his arm pits? Now what in the hell did that mean?

Thanks Sharita

The next evening as I was tidying up and preparing to leave for the day, I saw Jimmy strolling down the hallway. I intentionally met him face-to-face and saw his dilated pupils. I even thought I detected a faint smell of marijuana. Since I was accustomed to seeing him this way, I questioned my sense of smell and decided to go for a definitive answer.

"Time for another drug test, Jimmy," I said.

"Sure Mr. Stewart, no problemo, but this borders on harassment you know."

"Congratulations Jimmy. That may be the most intelligent thing I've heard you say since you've been here."

I gave him a test cup and a mirror to hold in front of him. As he stood there peeing into the cup, I heard Sharita's voice in my head, "Check his arm pits." Observing his urinating procedure, I noticed he would squeeze his elbows in toward his rib cage while I thought he was voiding his bladder. With every squeeze the stream would become more forceful. I walked up behind him, raised his arms, and felt under his arm pits.

"What's this?" I asked as I felt a ball under his arm. He jerked around to face me and inadvertently hosed-down my shoes.

"What you talking about man? That's just my arm."

I squeezed the contraption under his arm pit, and he sprayed some more.

"Man, you don't have to do this."

"Let's have it!" I demanded.

Jimmy took his off shirt and unfastened what appeared to be the rubber squeezable end to a blood pressure devise. A long plastic tube attached to it ran between his legs and was taped to his scrotum. It then extended to the end of his penis where it was attached with flesh-toned tape. Jimmy removed his pants and dropped his underwear, gingerly removing all the tape. I couldn't watch the painful procedure. He rolled the apparatus up and handed it toward me.

"I don't want to touch it. Just set it down," I said.

I put on a pair of latex gloves and placed it into a Wal-Mart bag I found under the sink. I had previously caught clients using toy baby bottles and other devices used to squirt water into a UA specimen cup. However, I caught them fairly quickly because the contained liquid was obviously not as warm as recently voided urine. The genius of Jimmy's concoction was that the unadulterated urine stayed warm because it was nestled in his arm pit. I also found out later that he used a friend's urine and kept a supply of fresh pee under his bed.

"What are you going to do man?" asked Jimmy in a defiant, but concerned tone.

"I'm going to present your violation to the team, but since I suspect you've been using the whole time you've been here, I'm going to recommend program failure and court sanctioning."

His voice cracked, "Will, will I go to jail?"

"That's a possibility, but only the judge can make that decision," I said.

"Man, I'm on a one-year suspended sentence. If I get revoked that's a year in the county jail. I'll get kicked out of school. My parents'll kill me!"

"You should have thought of that before you started playing this game and switching your UA samples. We've told you over and over again; if you have problems, talk to us. Talk to one of the team because we're here to help you be a success."

After Jimmy went back to his room and before I left for the day, I wrote a violation report. I also gave a copy of the citation to the dorm parents so that they would keep a closer watch on him. Even though justice was meted-out expeditiously in our program than regular probation, the report would still need to be filed with the prosecutor and court clerk. I planned to move him out of the dorm in the morning, but court action would take several days. After preparing the report, I started to have second thoughts.

Should I violate Jimmy or:
A. Forget the whole incident.
B. Make him confess to the class.
C. Get a patent on this ingenious devise and market it on the Internet.
D. Add other sanctions to his sentence like community service.
E. Recommend inpatient drug treatment.

I locked Jimmy's device in my file cabinet, logged my chronological entries into Jimmy's file and left for the day.

Too Early

"Mr. Stewart."

I didn't realize that I had already answered the phone. I gave a grunt to the noise on the end of the line. "This is Captain Taylor with the fire department. There's been a fire down at the college, and we'll need you to come down here and help straighten some things out."

Now I was awake. "Are you talking about our DUI program dorm? Is anyone hurt?"

"No, nobody's hurt, but there is a lot of damage. It was confined to the bottom floor. Seems the fire originated in your office. I'm afraid your office is a total loss."

Confused by my sleep hangover and the current events, I hung up the phone before I said, "Thank you captain, I'll be there as quick as I can."

The digital, halogen-lit clock glowed: "2:00 a.m."

When I arrived, the fire department was shoveling smoldering debris from my office. My clients were standing out under a tree; when I was spotted, several came running up to me.

"This is some bad shit."

"Yes, Dinky it is."

"Sorry about your office Mr. Stewart," said Sharita. "Me too," said Shakesha.

Stoney was leaning on a tree with his shirt off, cowboy hat pulled down and a cigarette hanging from the corner of his mouth. He tipped his hat and gave me the thumbs-up sign. The Huns, already on cell phones, gave me a disturbed and confused look as they tried to secure other dorm rooms on campus. According to the fire captain, because of the smoke and possible structural damage, it might be months before we could enter the dorm again.

The captain escorted me inside, and with flashlights we canvassed my office. "Looks to me like someone broke into your office and set it on fire."

He pulled an ash-colored piece of wood from under the carbon trash. "My best guess at this moment is, gasoline poured on your cabinet. We'll have official results as soon as possible. Whatever fool did this couldn't even tell the cabinets were fire proof."

"Yep captain, even I can smell the gasoline."

My office was a total loss. My framed certificates, plaques, and awards from drug court were either burnt to a crisp or melted into the floor. My computer, resembling a mole hill, was a melted lump on the floor. When I could no longer look at my wasted office, the captain and I returned to the breathable night air. I was enjoying the promising breeze until Cindy ran towards us.

"Mr. Stewart, Jimmy isn't here," she announced.

"Who's Jimmy?" inquired the captain.

"He's one of our clients and probably the only one with a good motive to do something like this."

An Unhappy Ending

There was nothing more that I could do. I went home but couldn't sleep. In the morning, I called Mr. Sheehy as soon as his office opened and told him the news. We arranged a meeting that afternoon with the team and all other stakeholders. After much painstaking debate and deliberation, we decided to abandon the program.

The university president carried the most weight in this discussion. The local newspapers and television stations were already announcing the fire as arson. Therefore, the president could not and would not accept the heat for allowing a program on campus that threatened student safety. I couldn't blame him. However, I did want him to recognize and appreciate the progress we had made. Hell, I wanted *him* to argue with Shakesha. I silently wondered if she would call him "whore" for shutting down the program.

That afternoon, the police called Mr. Sheehy's office. Jimmy Cohn had been arrested at his parent's house. Apparently Jimmy had snuck out of the dorm, gone to the closest all night convenience store and purchased a gallon of gasoline. He was seen on the store's video cameras making the purchase. Jimmy admitted his treacherous deed as well as the messy business with arm pit apparatus. Consequently, when his parents wouldn't bail him out of jail, he assaulted a jail officer and set his bunk on fire. In the end, he received a 25-year prison sentence for two counts of arson and felonious assault.

A Happy Ending

I was back working with a generic caseload of diverse clients about three months later and reasonably happy to be there. I planned to never volunteer for or specialize in anything in the future. After a week back on the job, I received a call over the intercom:

"Bill, come down to the conference room."

When I arrived, Mr. Sheehy greeted me along with my DUI team and sixteen of my old student clients. Attila and Hun gave me a certificate and trophy for my performance as a team leader, outstanding mentor, and probation officer. Additionally, the "Fearsome Foursome," my affectionate nickname for the dominant DUI student clients, made an appearance. Dinky still had his head phones on, Stoney had a new hat, and my favorites, Shakesha and Sharita, were still arguing. I felt at home.

"Mr. Stewart," Shakesha said, "we know we gave you a hard time and all but with your help, we're all alright. If you ever want to try this campus thing again, just give us a call, and we'll be there for you."

With that, I got a hug from the girls, and a thumbs up from Stoney. Dinky praised me with a, "You go, dude" and an air riff of a Jimi Hendrix's song.

Chapter Ten
"Reverse Perspective"

The Client

I don't understand why I always have to wait to see my probation officer. It's not like they're a doctor or somebody like that. It's the same every month. I report by the fifth, and each time I wait for at least thirty minutes. Today, I've been sitting here for an hour and fifteen minutes. When I arrived, I tried to read the two-week old newspaper, but I ended up creating dragons in my exhaled cigarette smoke in order to pass the time. About half of the familiar faces in the waiting room are also smoking cigarettes. Joe has his favorite pack, Camels, and Mary's flipping over her black and whites between a forefinger and thumb. The people who aren't smoking have a far off look in their eyes. They were probably smoking "something" before they came. I hope there's a candy bar machine around here to satisfy their cravings. I hate waiting. I wish I was like Matt over there. He just puts money into the kiosk automated reporting machine and leaves. He doesn't have to see his probation officer. Shit, he doesn't even have to take off his coat. Me? I have to wait in this crowded room to see my new probation officer, the fourth one since I was sentenced.

I've been on some form of probation my entire life. Well, since grade school anyway. In fourth grade, I hung out with a bunch of influential thugs. In fact, the school bully, Mark, was my best friend. Once a week, we'd get off the school bus and duck under a bridge in front of the school. Even though our hideout was only a few yards from the playground, the creek's bank hid us from the teachers and the principal. The muddy creek beneath the bridge seldom had more than a shallow stream running through it, but the bank was covered with six-foot-tall Johnson grass, worm infested elm trees, and an underbrush of black berry entanglements.

Mark and I would sit in the tall grass smoking stolen cigarettes and drinking anything we could find. Before settling into the bank, we would search the ditches by the nearby bars for liquor and wine bottles. Then we would pour anything we found into a large jelly jar. It always amazed me how much was left in throw-away bottles. On a good day we would collect a pint full of various brands of whiskey, vodka, gin, rum, and wine ... a strange yet tasty assortment. When I think back on those days, which isn't very often, the principal must have known we were there, but he never came looking for us. He was either afraid of us or just didn't give a damn ... maybe both.

Our hiding out and scavenging came to an abrupt halt one cool spring afternoon. As usual, I had provided the cigarettes, and we'd combined our collection efforts. It was almost time for school to get out when we noticed two trolls (what we called homeless people) walking towards us. Usually, the trolls pushed their shopping carts and looked for treasure: old clothing, a half-eaten sandwiches, or leftover take-out food. However, on this day, these two trolls weren't pushing shopping carts. The two men had raggedy shirts, long dirty jackets, and stocking caps. They didn't look like they were searching for any treasure. They shuffled towards us with their heads down and their hands in their pockets.

Mike and I threw rocks at the trolls and called them circus freaks. When they didn't react, we started to grow tired of harassing them. It wasn't fun if they didn't react. These guys didn't run like normal trolls, they just kept walking towards us. As they grew near, Mark, in his usual fearless tone, called the tall guy an ugly bastard and kicked dirt at him. The troll grabbed him and flung him to the ground. The other one reached for me, but I jumped into the creek and ran to the other side.

Now that I think about it, I ran across the creek without getting wet. I guess it was the adrenalin. Since I had escaped, the man turned to Mark. One troll pulled down Mark's pants as Mark franticly flailed at the man's ankles. I watched in horror as both trolls pinned Mark to the ground. The tall troll unzipped his pants and stood over Mark while the other man held him to the ground.

I though about running; I thought I should get help. Instead, I pulled out my pocketknife. No one was going to touch my friend! As I raced back across the creek, I opened the four-inch blade. I could feel my throbbing heartbeat in my shaking hands. With a quick leap from the middle of the creek, I jabbed the knife at the tall troll as his pants fell to his ankles. I stabbed him once in the neck as I fell to the ground. The other man who was holding Mark panicked when he saw the dark, red blood pulsating out of his fellow troll's neck. The injured man rolled off of Mark. He held his neck as blood squirted through his fingers and ran down his hand. Mark was covered in blood as he crawled from underneath the troll.

We ran up the bank towards the playground. Mark, trying to pull his pants up, reached the school before I did. We were running so hard that I didn't notice the school security guard as he came up and grabbed us. He scooped up Mark in his left arm and me in his right. The blood from the troll got all over the guard's white shirt.

I never really understood why, but a local judge declared Mark and I delinquents in desperate need of supervision. I think it was the half jar of assorted liquors they discovered at the creek. The injured troll died and the other one was never located. If it hadn't been for the fact that the tall troll had a record of sex crimes and that his pants were still down when he was found, I would have been charged with murder. Murder was way worse than my usual petty crimes; I'm only violent when someone is in trouble and needs my help.

Am I ever going to leave the waiting room? Where was I? Oh yeah ...

After the troll incident and before my high school graduation, I was arrested on several occasions for public drunkenness, possession of marijuana, and vandalism. Eventually, I graduated from high school because I wanted to make my mother proud. Even though I passed all my classes, I didn't learn nothing. I could read and write, but that was about it. My mom worked nights doing laundry for a nursing home, and my dad was a no-show loser. I knew my dad and saw him around town from time to time, but he never really talked to me. When I saw him at a Quik Stop my senior year, he asked how old I was and what kind of grades I was making. He smelled of tequila and stale clothing. I knew he didn't really care and wouldn't remember my age.

My first adult probation stint was a few years after high school. I was guilty and had no excuses. I thought stealing auto parts (particularly radios and mirrors) off of wrecked or impounded cars was a good idea, but I got greedy. On the third trip in one night, I encountered a pack of Dobermans. I learned the hard way that their guard dogs were only allowed to roam free after 2 a.m. The hellhounds came out of nowhere. I turned to get out of a 1970 GTO, and the pack of snarling animals crept out of the car's shadow. The lead dog bit my ankle and my thigh before I could lock myself in the car. I was relieved when the cops arrived and arrested me.

My court appointed attorney argued for diversion from formal prosecution, but to no avail. I guess my juvenile record wasn't so sealed after all. The judge stated he didn't want to give me a deferred sentence because he was sure I would screw it up in short order. I thought a sentence of probation was fine and was happy to get it. I didn't even care if the restitution he ordered seemed excessive for the sixteen radios and the truckload of mirrors I had stolen. I should've read the fine print; the court costs, fines, victim's compensation charge, DNA testing, and other fees totaled more than $7,000.

I accepted my five-year suspended sentence and reported to the probation intake office on the eighth floor of the courthouse. I knew right away this was going to be different from juvenile probation. When I walked in, I was handed a stack of forms and told to sit down and fill them out. If I couldn't read or write, I was to ask one of the other stooges going through intake to assist me. After I found a pencil and a chair, my attorney bid me farewell, wished me good luck, and said see you soon.

I didn't understand half the questions I was answering. However, I was relieved to discover that none of my fellow probation recruits were doing quality work on their forms. They would simply hand their stack of forms to an officer and then they were given directions to the probation office closest to their homes. Since no one checked the forms, I marked the wrong race and sex on mine. I turned the stuff in and was told I had 48 hours to report to my probation office.

When I reported, the receptionist couldn't find my paperwork. Finally a stern-looking officer, claiming that I didn't look like an Asian woman, retrieved me from the waiting room. I told him that I was indeed a man, and there was obviously some sort of confusion. My officer was young, maybe younger than me, and didn't think I was funny.

He must have been proud of his accomplishments. His college diploma, probation school certificate, and Rotary Club membership plaque were hanging on his office wall. He also had a picture of his wife and baby on his desk. I told him it probably wasn't a good idea to have everyone see what his wife and child looked like. He looked at me as if I was crazy and he felt like I was trying to intimidate him. I assured him that I wouldn't be a problem, and I expressed my concern about the amount of restitution and fees. He sharply reminded me that I must have agreed to these terms, or I wouldn't have gotten probation. Also, if I failed to pay, he would request a revocation of my probation.

I asked him if he understood how public defenders operated and that I only saw mine twice, once prior to my release on bond and again at sentencing for a total of 15 minutes. I explained how the judge didn't mention the additional fees until after sentencing. Nevertheless, this young prepster ignored me. He asked me to sign some sort of orientation verification, handed me his business card, and said he would see me next month by the fifth. The whole meeting took 15 minutes, the longest meeting I ever had with him.

In order to pay my restitution and other fees, I started working at a fast service oil and lube franchise where I barely made minimum wage. After taxes and insurance, I brought home about $400 every two weeks. My restitution and other assorted court-related costs were $200 per month. Needless to say, I was going to have difficulty paying. Besides the court-ordered financial obligations I had, I shared the cost of an old apartment with two other guys, and I had to pay for my 1979 Impala. I was able to make the first three restitution payments on time, but then I fell behind.

On my next visit to my probation officer, I decided to tell him how difficult it was to make the payments and ask if I could do anything about it. He listened for about ten seconds, nodded his head, and asked me to produce a urine sample. Since my officer obviously didn't care about my financial troubles, I came right out and told him my urine would probably be dirty because I had smoked pot a few days before with a bunch of my friends. He tested it anyway, and the test came back positive. Even though I was busted for smoking pot, at least I proved to him that I was honest. The next week I was arrested at work for violating my probation.

Luckily (I thought at the time), I didn't go before the same judge. Except this time because I'd been working, I didn't qualify for a public defender. So, I did like anyone else who couldn't post bond and was denied release pending my hearing. I threw myself to the mercy of the court. There were hundreds of people in for revocation hearings that day who were in the same predicament as me.

When it was my turn, I told the judge I was guilty and would be representing myself. He called my probation officer and a young attorney, who had been representing several other revocation clients that day, to the bench. He asked the attorney to consult with me. After we chatted for about two minutes, my new attorney approached the bench and entered my plea of guilty.

At that point, the judge asked my probation officer if he believed I should have my probation revoked. My young, outstanding Rotarian probation officer stated I had an extensive juvenile record and that my lack of seriousness for the system, failure to pay restitution, and my drug usage were clear indicators I hadn't learned anything since my sentencing and that I had simply graduated from a life of juvenile to adult crime.

He also told the judge that I'd been intimidating and that I would benefit from incarceration. I advised the judge that I had several friends who had been in prison, and I didn't think they had benefited at all. Since I had pled guilty, the judge told me there would be no testimony from me unless I changed my plea. I assured the judge I was guilty, but I didn't think the severity of my violations warranted prison.

I guess six months in the prison boot camp for young adults was a compromise. It wasn't a pleasant experience, and I don't like thinking about it. It was six months of my life that I'll never get back, and I didn't learn a damn thing. The boot camp looked like my high school only with a razor wire fence and guards patrolling it. Many of my fellow inmates were trolls in training with no expectations for their future.

I spent most of my stay picking up cigarette butts and cleaning toilets. We did push ups in the mud and marched in formation twice a day. One of our drill sergeants was a likable enough guy who most of us respected. He was a retired military man and kept reminding us that our boot camp wasn't nearly as tough as army boot camp. At least the army takes care of its soldiers after their initiation into the system; revocation camp simply tossed me back onto the streets with only a probation officer to watch over me.

I can't believe this. Joe and Mary have seen their officers. In fact, Mary is already done. I feel as though I've been sitting here for two days! Maybe I should just get up and leave, but if I leave I might get sent back to the boot camp. This sucks!

I was released from prison boot camp and put back on probation four months to the day I entered. I reported to my newly assigned probation office for two months before I met my official officer, Tony Hill. This guy was a retired police officer who could have cared less about anything related to me or my situation. Each time we met, I was in and out of his office in five minutes.

He would ask the same three questions every month: Have I been arrested? Have I changed residences? Are there any other changes? I would always answer no, no, and what do you mean by changes? He would just nod his head, obviously not listening to my last comment, and would bid me farewell.

One time while waiting for Officer Hill, I met a young man in the waiting room who was obviously strung out on drugs and having a terrible time. He looked like he was having some sort of permanent panic attack. He was sweating and trembling. I'd done enough drugs to recognize the signs of a potential overdose.

We visited for a little while and I discovered we had the same probation officer. I don't know why, but when he was called to see Officer Hill, I asked to go with him. The receptionist didn't seem to mind, so I guided my new buddy to Officer Hill's office. I really didn't expect Officer Hill to give two hoots about my new friend. In fact, Officer Hill didn't even notice that the guy was pale and his eyes were dilated to the max.

Officer Hill would have had to look at him for that to happen. I made my waiting room buddy tell Officer Hill he was using and needed help. Officer Hill ignored both of us and asked his usual three questions. Again, my buddy said he was strung out. Officer Hill advised him to try to do better and come back next month by the fifth, and they would discuss the issue again.

That's when I realized Officer Hill was already retired. He was determined to work only from nine to five, and no one or anything was going to interrupt his routine. When we left, we found a city rescue mission that gave us a lead on a possible detoxification center. My buddy made the connection, and I never saw him again. I always look for him while I'm sitting in the waiting room.

I didn't expect and didn't receive any assistance from my probation officer when I, once again, failed to pay restitution and failed two more drug tests. Officer Hill didn't ask me if I had a drug problem, but he did arrest me unexpectedly. This time the judge revoked eight months from my suspended sentence, and sent me to jail. I spent only seven days in jail before I was transferred to a halfway house. With earned and achievement credits for completing a basic life skills program, I was back on the streets and returned to my suspended sentence status within months. And now I have to meet my new probation officer.

The Officer

I didn't think the day could get any busier. I was at least an hour behind, and my daughter kept calling to ask if she could go out for dinner. To top it off, my car was in the shop, I couldn't get a rental and my stupid computer had a virus. Nevertheless, I was surviving. I've been through worse. At least the computer and car could be fixed, and I told my daughter that she could stay out till ten.

I dropped out of high school my senior year to get married. I just didn't want to deal with all the bullshit requirements to graduate. Besides, I was nine months pregnant and no graduation gown was going to hide that. The school didn't let me do home study, so I finished school at an adult learning center. It was at the center that I had my first encounters with probation officers and their clients.

Many of my classmates were on probation and sometimes a probation officer would be at the door to verify their attendance. These probation clients were no different than the classmates I hung out with in high school. They had many of the same problems but apparently dealt with them in an inappropriate way; either stealing stuff or smoking weed. Many of them were older than me, yet stuck in their childhoods. I tutored some and gave advice to others.

When my daughter was four years old, my husband traded me in for a younger model, and we got divorced. My mother warned me that older men, particularly him, couldn't keep their hands off of young women. Nevertheless, we got married because I was pregnant, and we got divorced because his latest fling was pregnant.

At the divorce proceedings, we fought for custody of our daughter. My grant writing job at a local non-profit community service agency barely paid the bills, and my ex-husband made sure that the judge knew that I was in a financial slump. He worked at his family's lucrative hardware business and made a good living while I was 22 years old and feeling like I was forty.

I was astounded when I lost custody of my child and was given the visiting rights that my ex once had. The judge ruled that my husband could better care for our child because I had to have several different babysitters and daycares to watch my daughter during the day. The judge was really trying to say that I didn't make enough money, and my lack of funds to secure an attorney wouldn't get me anywhere in his courtroom. Of course it didn't help that my ex was able to obtain a change of venue to a court where his family was well known. For the first time in my life, I felt like a victim. I also felt the wrath of discrimination.

I complied with the court order and, with much resolve, decided to address my life head on in order to be considered a proper mother for my child. I didn't like being a victim, so I enrolled in college part-time and picked up extra work as an English composition tutor on campus. Six years later I had a college degree in human relations and a minor in English. I took my degree and went out into the world to find and start a career. With my thirtieth birthday just around the corner, I wanted a financially secure, fulfilling, and full-time job.

I applied for every job remotely related or connected to my degree. Six months later I was still looking. I had a part time job at the adult education center where I had gotten my GED, but I wanted more. One evening after class, I met a probation officer who occasionally dropped in to verify attendance of his probationers. He told me his department was hiring and invited me to fill out an application. I was intrigued that probation officers could be women, so I decided to apply. I took a written test a week later. I had my first promising prospect for a real job.

The test appeared to be a lot of common sense questions and hypothetical situations. They were all multiple choice questions with one exception. I was asked to write 150 words on why I wanted to be a probation officer. I was told the content wasn't important but rather they wanted to ascertain whether or not I could write and spell. Since I had been an English tutor, I passed with flying colors. Two months later a portly old man interviewed me for an officer position. He spit when he talked and asked many diverse questions.

He asked me questions like: How would I respond if a client made a pass at me or could I recommend prison for someone who had numerous positive drug tests?

He wanted to know: Did I believe in capital punishment? Would I support the simple possession of marijuana being decriminalized? Could I take a person's life in self-defense or in the defense of others?

In addition: Could I tell a judge "No" if he or she told me what to recommend on a pre-sentence investigation or on a violation report? And, as a woman, would I feel comfortable doing home visits on clients alone?

Like other interviews, he also wanted to know my strengths and weaknesses, my biases and prejudices. The real hardcore question was whether I believed people could change. I figured that if I could change, anyone could. There were many other questions but I was too overwhelmed to remember them all.

I thought I screwed up the question about believing in capital punishment. When I get nervous I sometimes inappropriately use humor. I answered, quoting Edith Bunker, "As long as it is not too severe." He didn't laugh and I thought I'd blown the interview.

Even though I didn't say everything that I thought he wanted to hear, I was called back for a conformation interview with the chief probation officer and several of his staff. This interview was as difficult as the first and the questions were more open ended. They seemed more concerned with post-hiring behavior than my past.

Their major concerns centered on whether I would attend eight weeks of training, be able to work evenings, and be available after hours. I must have convinced them that I would be a wonderful probation officer because a week later I was getting a physical and having my background checked. I was also scheduled to submit to a psychological examination that utilized the Minnesota Multiphasic Personality Inventory.

I survived the officer training with its excessive schooling in court room demeanor, conducting assessments, specialty courts, substance abuse treatment, motivational interviewing, policies and procedures, self-defense, first-aid, CPR, and report writing. I was overwhelmed with the avalanche of information, but I survived, graduating first in my class.

As a graduation present, I received my first caseload: 123 assorted clients from a caseload that hadn't had an assigned officer for three months. My first job was to transcribe into each of their files a chronological record based on the past three months of client monthly reports and officer's notes. In addition to getting a feel and control of my caseload, I also had duty officer assignments and pre-sentence investigations to conduct. Many of my clients were glad to have a permanent officer while some couldn't give a damn one way or the other.

Once I became a probation officer, my self-confidence, drive, and determination were seriously challenged. I'd often question whether I had anything to offer my clients. After all, what did I know about their problems and difficulties? However, I did find enjoyment in the ever-changing position of a probation officer and the constant variety of situations I encountered. One day, I'd deal with a client who felt his pit bull was an excellent driver, and the next I'd find a homeless shelter for an unfortunate client. I guess I really did love experiencing a new challenge and a new adventure each day.

Today was no exception, and I just had to settle down and see what the system would bring to me.

The Officer and Client

My caseload was now at about 140 active bodies and continuing to grow. All of my absconders and low level cases were transferred to an administrative caseload. I received several new additions to my caseload a week ago, and I expected a few of my new clients to be reporting in. The first one, Barry Stone, showed up at noon and had waited an hour and a half to see me. He was on a five-year suspended sentence that had been partially revoked twice. He had served time in a boot camp for young offenders. I didn't know what to expect from him, but I suspected he was a street smart kid who grew up making all the wrong choices. I uncovered his file on my desk and walked to the waiting room.

"Mr. Stone, you're next."

A rather small, but muscular blond-haired young man stood up and walked towards me. I had expected a tattooed, long-haired and unkempt individual, but what I encountered was a man who called me ma'am.

"How are you today, Mr. Stone?" I asked while I walked him to my office and introduced myself.

"Oh, I've had better days. I'm glad to be out of prison." He took his baseball cap off of his head and held it behind his back.

"Well, that's a good thing," I replied. "I'd be concerned if you liked prison."

He gave a quick smile, taking note of my light-hearted response. As we continued towards my office, Mr. Stone walked with an air of confidence and looked only straight ahead. Once he entered my office, he quickly scanned his surroundings.

"Mr. Stone, are you looking for something?" I asked.

"I've learned you can tell a lot about your probation officer by what they have in their office. You don't have much of anything, just some AA and NA meeting dates, job listings, and GED class schedules."

"What were you expecting?"

He put his hat in his lap and continued to look around, paying particular attention to the magnets on the file cabinet.

"I didn't expect much *from you.* I just like to look around."

I didn't like his cynical response. "Well, Mr. Stone, your low expectations will make my job fairly easy. If you expect nothing from me, then the pressure will be all on you. You see, I do expect a great deal from you."

"I don't have any pressure." He leaned back in the chair.

"That could be one of your problems. Expecting nothing of yourself is the only way to have no pressure."

"Whatever, Ms. Harris. Isn't it about time for me to go? Don't you have some hidden timer to let you know when five minutes are up? I think I have reached my limit."

He stood up to leave, and this time *I* leaned back in my chair. "What gave you that idea? We have a lot to go over today, so please sit down."

"Look, I don't mean to be disrespectful, but I had to wait forever to see you and I've been here several times before. Here's the deal. I come in once per month for five minutes; you ask me if I've had any arrests or changed employment. I tell you no on all counts, and then you say, see you next month."

"Mr. Stone, there have been some changes since you were sent to the halfway house. Now, you'll have to suck it up and spend as much time as it takes for you and me to figure out how to keep you out of prison."

"I can save both of us time and bullshit. Just go ahead and recommend a full revocation of what's left of my suspended sentence."

He plopped back down in the chair, waiting for me to respond to his challenge.

"Now why would I want to do that?"

"You don't get it do you?" he said.

Apparently I didn't, so I motioned for him to enlighten me.

"I agreed to the suspended sentence and restitution and all that other financial stuff to get out of jail and get this over with. The prosecutor laid all of that on me knowing I couldn't make those high monthly payments. The whole thing was a set up from the beginning. I get a job, try to do right, get on my feet a little and "Bam!" I'm off to prison. I get out and history repeats itself. It is like deja vu all over again, like Yogi Berra said."

He finished his spiel while I flipped through his file.

"Were the drug tests part of the set-up?" I didn't even look up at him. I just continued to flip through his file.

"No, I did that on my own. I notice you have a coke on your desk. How often you drink them?"

I thought he was trying to change the subject.

"I probably drink three a day."

"Would it be hard for you to just up and stop drinking them?" he asked.

I now knew where this conversation was going. "Yes, but I would stop if drinking pop would put me in prison."

Defeated by his failed analogy, he uncomfortably squirmed in his chair. However, his tone became more amiable.

"Using pot is my bad habit, like drinking coke's your habit. I don't think you are addicted to them any more than I am to pot. Pot's just more accepted in my environment than yours."

"If that's the case," I said, "we need to re-examine your environment or, at least, your leisure time to stop history from repeating itself. Now, enough small talk. We have some work to do. We're going to start off with an updated orientation, review your rules and conditions of supervision, complete an updated assessment, and develop a case plan."

"Been there, done that. You fill it out, and I'll sign it."

I just shook my head. "This is as much for my benefit as yours. We should both have an understanding of expectations, and you, my friend, will help me identify the steps necessary to successfully terminate your sentence. First let's talk about your employment. Where do you work now?"

"I haven't had time to look for a job, but finding one won't be hard. I can walk into any fast food place or restaurant and get a job."

"Is that what you want, to work at minimum wage all your life? There's no problem with that, but I was looking at your vocational assessment score and I.Q. results from when you were in the prison boot camp. You appear to be much more capable."

He laughed uncontrollably and placed his feet on my desk. As I moved the files from under his feet, he put his heals back on the floor.

"If working at fast food places are OK with you, then that's fine. However, with the restitution and fees you owe, you might consider something with more wage potential. You could still work minimum wage and go to vocational school so you can get a better job."

"I ain't got money to go to school and besides, you know it is just a matter of time before I go back to prison."

"Mr. Stone, I've seen a lot of victims and losers in my time and you don't look like any of them. You have choices. Didn't you complete a cognitive behavior program in prison?"

"Yeah ... I got a certificate and finished sooner than everyone else."

"Yes, but did you learn anything?"

He thought for awhile and nodded his head.

"Take the information you have and apply it," I suggested. "For example, if you've been revoked twice for failure to pay restitution, wouldn't it make sense to change your employment and increase your income? Also, if you're just hanging out with your buddies and smoking dope, wouldn't it make sense to maybe quit hanging out with that crowd? What will it take to make you successful this time around? If it didn't work last time, then why not change it?"

"So, you want me to tell you what to write on the case plan?"

"Yes, Mr. Stone, now you're getting it. I can't do this probation for you, but what I can do is help you help yourself. Did you know that since you're out of prison you probably qualify for a federal PELL grant to pay your school tuition? You *could* go back to school."

He rolled his eyes as if I just told him a real whopper. "That's all fine and good, but I'll be behind on restitution before I get a job and receive my first pay check. Besides, I'll have to work so much I ain't got time for school."

"We can deal with that. If you show me that you're willing to address the causes of your previous failures, then I'll request an extension for your restitution payments."

"Sounds good to me," he said as he got up again to leave.

"Not so quick, Mr. Stone. I have another challenge for you. Before I put my good name on the line for you, you must prove to me that you can stop smoking dope. Stay negative for three months on your drug tests, and we can discuss a recommendation to reduce the monthly payment amount on your fees. And, if you come up positive, you agree to attend substance abuse therapy sessions."

"Man, I don't know; sounds like I'm giving a lot. Besides, I've lost count of how many probation officers I've had. You'll probably be gone next month, and no officer in their right mind is going to make the same deal you just did."

"Your officer should make no difference. It's you, Mr. Stone, who creates a positive outcome."

"Ms. Harris, why don't you write on the case plan that I'll not be positive for drugs, and I'll enroll in school if I get a grant."

So what's next?

A.   Immediately transfer him to another officer.

B.   Prepare a violation report, as it is just a matter of time.

C.   Ask him to come back in a week to review progress.

D.   Refer him to an employment counselor.

E.   Tell him you were just joking and ask the three basic questions.

F.   Tell him not to report for a year as he had just used-up a full year of your time in probation officer contact calculations.

G.   Ask him when he thought he needed to see you again.